D0434042

SpongeBob SquarePants™

Fool's Gold

TITAN BOOKS

SPONGEBOB SQUAREPANTS: FOOL'S GOLD

ISBN: 9781845769048

Stories & Scripts: Graham Annable, Craig Boldman, Chris Duffy, KC Green,
Amy Keating-Rogers, James Kolchalka, Jacob Lambert,
David Lewman, Patrick O'Donnell, Gregg Schigiel
Pencils & inks: Jeff Albrecht, Graham Annable,
Vincent Deporter, James Kolchalka, Jose Marzan Jr., Gregg Schigiel
Colours: Graham Annable, Wes Dzioba, James Kolchalka, Sno Cone Studios
Letters: Graham Annable, Comicraft, James Kolchalka

Published by Titan Books,
A division of Titan Publishing Group Ltd.
144 Southwark St.
London SE1 0UP

© 2010 Viacom International. All rights reserved. Nickolodeon, SpongeBob SquarePants and all related titles, logos and characters are trademarks of Viacom International Inc.
Created by Stephen Hillenburg.

No portion of this book may be reproduced or transmitted in any form or by any means, without the express written permission of the publisher. Names, characters, places and incidents featured in this publication are either the product of the author's imagination or used fictitiously. Any resemblance to actual persons, living or dead (except for satirical purposes), is entirely coincidental.

A CIP catalogue record for this title is available from the British Library.

This edition first published: July 2010

1 3 5 7 9 10 8 6 4 2

Printed in China.

Also available from Titan:

SpongeBob SquarePants: Gone JellyFishing (ISBN: 9781845762230)
SpongeBob SquarePants: Mermaid to Measure (ISBN: 9781845762247)
SpongeBob SquarePants: My Pet Sea Monster (ISBN: 9781845764678)

What did you think of this book? We love to hear from our readers. Please email us at: readerfeedback@titanemail.com, or write to us at the above address.
You can also visit us at: **www.titanbooks.com**

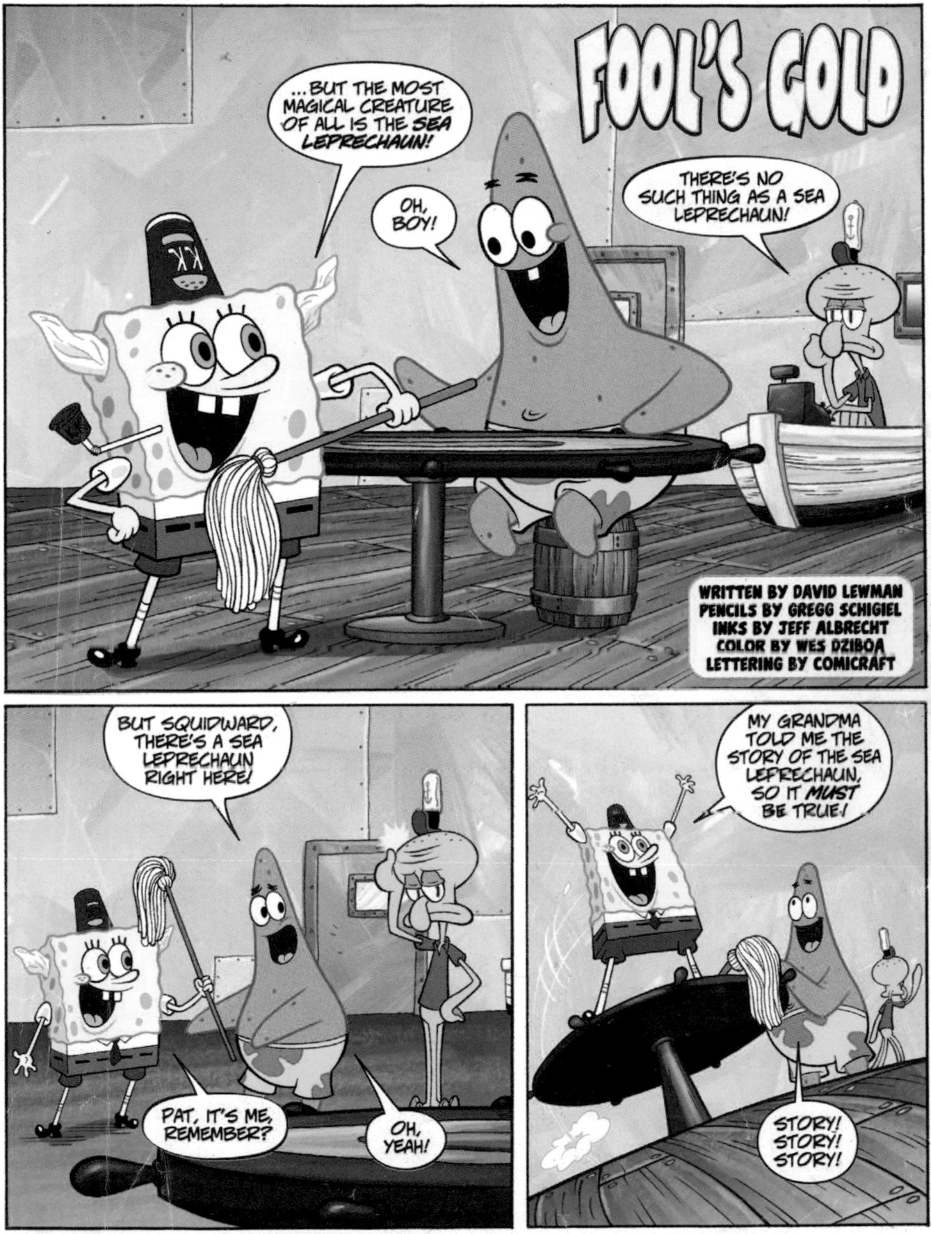

FOOL'S GOLD

...BUT THE MOST MAGICAL CREATURE OF ALL IS THE *SEA LEPRECHAUN!*

OH, BOY!

THERE'S NO SUCH THING AS A SEA LEPRECHAUN!

WRITTEN BY DAVID LEWMAN
PENCILS BY GREGG SCHIGIEL
INKS BY JEFF ALBRECHT
COLOR BY WES DZIBOA
LETTERING BY COMICRAFT

THE SEA LEPRECHAUN IS VERY SHY...

...BUT IF YOU FIND HIM, GRAB HIS TAIL AND HOLD ON TIGHT!
HEY, WATCH IT, PAL!

HE JUST MAY LEAD YOU TO HIS POT OF GOLD...
...OR SO THEY SAY!
OOOOH! POT OF GOLD!
PLEASE STOP SPITTING IN MY SOUP.

BAM!
POT OF GOLD?!
WHERE?!!!

ONLY THE SEA LEPRECHAUN KNOWS, MR. KRABS!
THEN GO CATCH HIM!
NOW!

AND SO...
I DON'T GET IT. WHY ARE WE PUTTING YOUR SHOES ON THE SIDEWALK?
THE SEA LEPRECHAUN LOVES REPAIRING SHOES. HE WON'T BE ABLE TO RESIST!
OHHHHHH!
I DON'T GET IT.

ANY MINUTE NOW, THE SEA LEPRECHAUN WILL COME TO FIX MY SHOES...

ANY MINUTE NOW...

COCKADOODLE-DOO!

LOOK, SPONGEBOB! SOMEONE LEFT A NOTE BY YOUR SHOES!
IT'S FROM HIM!

"DEAR SPONGE PERSON: YOUR SHOES DON'T NEED ANY REPAIRS. SIGNED, THE SEA LEPRECHAUN."
WHO'S IT FROM?

THIS SEA LEPRECHAUN TRAP CAN'T FAIL!
THEN IT SHOULD GO TO SCHOOL!
Welcome Sea Leprechaun

NOW WE BAIT THE TRAP WITH LUCKY KELP CEREAL.
Welcome Sea Leprechaun
LUCKY KELP

THE NEXT MORNING...
AH-HA! IT WORKED! WE CAUGHT A...
Welcome Sea Leprechaun

...PATRICK?
Welcome Sea Leprechaun
I GOT HUNGRY.

THE *NEXT* NEXT MORNING...
IT WORKED AGAIN!
Welcome Sea Leprechaun
AND WE FINALLY CAUGHT...

MR. KRABS?
I CAN'T RESIST A FREE BREAKFAST.
Welcome Sea Leprechaun
LUCKY KELP

THE NEXT NEXT NEXT MORNING...
PLANKTON?
IF KRABS HAS IT, I WANT IT!
Welcome Sea Leprechaun
LUCKY KELP

I THINK WE NEED A NEW PLAN, PATRICK.
AND A NEW BOX OF CEREAL.

PSST!
WANNA BUY SOME COOL SUNGLASSES?
NO, KIND VENDOR.
WE'RE TOO BUSY HUNTING THE SHY SEA LEPRECHAUN AND HIS MYTHICAL POT OF GOLD.

DID I SAY SUNGLASSES? I MEANT SEA LEPRECHAUN GLASSES! PUT 'EM ON, AND YOU'LL SEE THE LEPRECHAUN!
SOLD!

NOW REMEMBER, DON'T PUT 'EM ON UNTIL I'M OUT OF SIGHT.
RIGHT! THANK YOU!

NOTHING... I THINK THAT GUY CHEATED US.
SPONGEBOB! YOU'RE A SEA LEPRECHAUN!

BARNACLES. WE'LL NEVER FIND THE SEA LEPRECHAUN... NEVER SEE HIS GREEN TAIL...
... NEVER HEAR HIS BEAUTIFUL WHISTLING...

WHAT'D YOU SAY, SPONGEBOB? I CAN'T HEAR YOU OVER THE BEAUTIFUL WHISTLING.
THE SEA LEPRECHAUN!

WOW, A WHISTLING ROCK!
NO, PATRICK, THE SEA LEPRECHAUN MUST BE BACK THERE...

I...

...GOT HIM!!!
YEAH!

GAH!
HI, GRANDMA!
THE SEA LEPRE-CHAUN
WHOA!!
OOF!
YOW!

LET...
...GO...
...O' ME...
...TAIL!
BONK!
KONK!
NEVER...

ALL RIGHT, ALL RIGHT, FINE! THEN I'LL GIVE YE ME--
POT OF--
GOLD!!!

HERE YOU GO, MR. KRABS.
OH BOY OH BOY OH BOY!

COME TO PAPA, YOU BEAUTIFUL GO--
HUH?

SHE'S ALL YOURS, SPONGEBOB.

I GUESS THE STORIES WERE WRONG. IT'S NOT A POT OF GOLD--IT'S EVEN BETTER!
A POT OF MOLD!
YAY!
END

PIZZA TIP
DING DONG!

YAY! PIZZA!

DING DONG!
OKAY, I'LL GET IT...

HEY, THERE! THANKS A LOT!

A-HEM!
I THINK HE WANTS THE MONEY!

OH, YEAH!

HERE YOU GO. ELEVEN DOLLARS, ON THE NOSE.

A-HEM!
DO YOU NEED A LOZENGE?
I THINK HE WANTS A TIP!

HEH, HEH... ONE MOMENT, PLEASE!

TOSS
RUN!

TOSS
THROW

SMASH

Y'KNOW, YOU SHOULD ALWAYS KEEP A LITTLE EXTRA MONEY AROUND IN CASE OF AN EMERGENCY!
PULL
PULL

THANKS!!

SLAM!

??

"ALWAYS KEEP A LITTLE EXTRA MONEY AROUND..." THAT'S THE BEST TIP I'VE GOTTEN ALL NIGHT!!
END

BASEMENT
WE'RE READY TO PLAY YOUR FUN GAME, MR. KRABS!
GOOD! THE NAME O'THE GAME IS "CLEAN ME BASEMENT!"

DO A GOOD JOB, 'CAUSE I'M SICK OF LOSIN' THINGS DOWN THERE. AN' REMEMBER, BOYS...
...DON'T THROW ANYTHING AWAY!
AYE-AYE, MR. KRABS!

BOY, THIS BASEMENT SURE IS FULL. WHAT CAN WE DO WITH ALL THIS STUFF, PATRICK?
HMM...

I'LL HANDLE THIS!
PATRICK, NO!!!

I KNOW! MAYBE THE CLEAN-UP FAIRY WILL COME AND HELP US!
CLEAN-UP FAIRY? THAT'S BABY STUFF, SPONGEBOB.

WELL, I GUESS WE WON'T BE NEEDING YOU, CLEAN-UP FAIRY.
WHAT. EVER.

MANY IDEAS LATER...
HEY, SPONGEBOB! I MADE ALL THE JUNK GO AWAY!

NOW YOU TRY IT!

TARTAR SAUCE. IT STOPPED WORKING.
WAIT! I'VE GOT A GREAT IDEA!

AND SOON...
ALL DONE, MR. KRABS! YOU'LL NEVER HAVE TROUBLE FINDING YOUR STUFF AGAIN!
REALLY?

HMM... NOT BAD!
WELL, OFF TO BED!
I'LL SLEEP LIKE A GUPPY, WITH THAT MESS OUTTA ME WAY!
THE END

DOMINOS!
THESE GIANT DOMINOES SURE WERE A GREAT IDEA, HUH?
AND THEY ONLY COST YOU TWO MONTHS PAY!

SO, YOU READY?
YOU CAN SAY THAT AGAIN!
SO, YOU READY?
HUH?

HERE WE GO!

STEADY...

ALL THIS WORK IS REALLY TONING MY FRIBULOIDS!
I FEEL IT IN MY GLUTICEPS.

WHEW!
THAT'S IT! SHALL WE?
LET'S SHALL!

THIS IS THE ONLY WAY TO TRAVEL!
CLACK
CLACK
CLACK
CLACKITY
END

IRKSOME
SNZZZ...

SQUIIIDWARRD...
SNRK??

SQUIDWARD!!
OH, NO...

SPONGEBOB! DO YOU HAVE ANY IDEA WHAT TIME IT IS? THIS HAD BETTER BE AN EMERGENCY!
I DON'T! AND IT IS! I NEED HELP FINISHING MY CROSSWORD PUZZLE!

WHAT'S ANOTHER WORD FOR 'IRKSOME'?
ARE YOU SERIOUS?

YES, YES, YES! IF I DON'T FIGURE OUT ANOTHER WORD FOR 'IRKSOME,' I'LL GO CRAZY!!

WELL, YOU'RE MAKING ME GO CRAZY! IT'S THREE A.M., AND YOU'RE ASKING ME FOR ANOTHER WORD FOR 'IRKSOME'!

GOOD NIGHT, SPONGEBOB! YOU'RE REALLY ANNOYING!
SLAM!

"YOU'RE REALLY ANNOYING!"

"REALLY ANNOYING!"

"ANNOYING!"

OH, WELL. I GUESS I'LL NEVER FIGURE OUT ANOTHER WORD FOR 'IRKSOME.'
END

SPONGEBOB DREAM PANTS
ZZZZZ...
WRITTEN BY KC GREEN
PENCILS BY GREGG SCHIGIEL
INKS BY JEFF ALBRECHT
COLOUR BY WES DZIBOA
LETTERING BY COMICRAFT

LATER THAT MORNING...
OH, PATRICK! YOU WOULDN'T BELIEVE THE DREAM I HAD!

"I FLEW A KRABBY PATTY AROUND A GIANT SPACE EYE, THEN LANDED IN THE KRUSTY KRAB TO HAVE LUNCH WITH SOME GHOSTS!"

IT WAS AMAZING!

HOW DO YOU KNOW YOU'RE STILL NOT DREAMING?

WELL, I THINK I WOKE UP THIS MORNING...
NOW I'M NOT SO SURE!

QUICK, PATRICK! GIVE ME A PINCH!!

PINCH
YEEOUCH!

THAT WAS ONE HECK OF A PINCH, PATRICK.

SO, ARE YOU AWAKE YET?
I DUNNO... PINCH ME *AGAIN!*

PEEEENCH

MAYBE WE NEED SOMETHING HARDER TO PINCH YOU WITH.

ZZZ...

ZZZZZ...

THOOM!
AAH!

WHAT A NIGHTMARE! I THOUGHT MY HOUSE WAS TILTING, ALL OF A SUDD--

THOOM!
AAAHHH!

SMASH

COOL.

PATRICK! WHAT IN NEPTUNE'S NAME ARE YOU DOING?!

WE'RE MAKING SURE SPONGEBOB'S NOT DREAMING! PINCHING DIDN'T HELP, SO I DROPPED YOUR HOUSE ON HIM!

I THINK IT WORKED, PATRICK! ALL THIS PAIN I'M EXPERIENCING MUST MEAN I'M AWAKE!

HOORAY!

WELL, THAT'S JUST GREAT. NOW, WILL YOU IDIOTS PLEASE PUT MY HOUSE UPRIGHT SO I CAN GO BACK TO SLEEP?!

SPONGEBOB!
WHAT IF SQUIDWARD IS STILL DREAMING?!

OH, MY GOSH! YOU MAY BE RIGHT, PATRICK!

LET'S PINCH HIM, JUST IN CASE!

UH-OH.

PINCH
PINCH
END

PLUGS
HEY, NICE HOLES!
HUH?!

STUPID HOLES...

MAYBE IF I PLUG 'EM NO ONE WILL NOTICE.
BUT WITH WHAT...?

SEANUT BUTTER'S TOO DRIPPY...
SEANUT BUTTER

KELP'S TOO SMELLY...

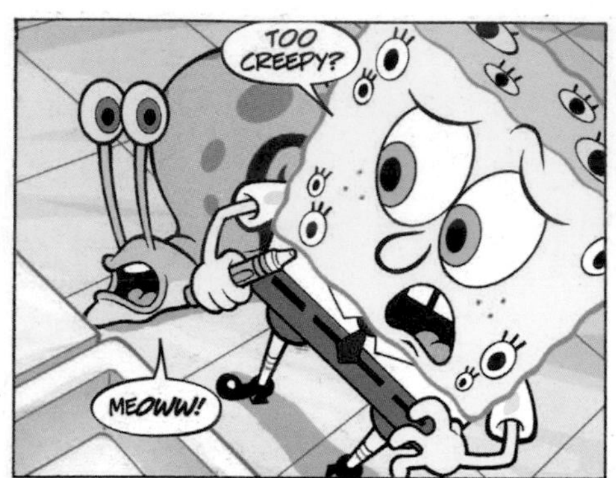
TOO CREEPY?
MEOWW!

HI, SANDY!
SPONGEBOB, DID YOU PLUG ALL YER HOLES WITH CORKS?!

UM, WHAT HOLES?
THERE'S NOTHING WRONG WITH SPONGES HAVING HOLES.
WHY, YOU SHOULD LOVE 'EM!

SANDY'S RIGHT!
I LOVE HOLES!!!
BUS
POP!
PLINK!
PLUNK!

YAAAAAHHHH!
THE END

MAGIC BEANS!
DING DOING
WHO COULD THAT BE?

HELLO, MY GOOD SPONGE!
UM... HI...

MORTON J. SEASQUIRT, AT YOUR SERVICE! I'M HERE TO OFFER YOU A *TRULY* ONCE-IN-A-LIFETIME OPPORTUNITY!! YES, YOU *GUESSED* IT...

...MAGIC BEANS!

MAGIC *BEANS*?!

YEP!! JUST PLANT THEM AND THEY'LL GROW STRAIGHT UP TO THE SKY!

AND...UM...THEY CAN ALSO DO LOTS OF *OTHER*...UM... *MAGIC STUFF*...

TWO MINUTES LATER...
WHEW! TOUGH SALE! FOR A SECOND THERE, I THOUGHT THOSE SUCKERS WERE *ONTO* ME!

BOY, THESE MAGIC BEANS ARE *AMAZING!*
I KNOW! HOW COULD MORTON J. SEASQUIRT *EVER* GET RID OF THEM?

PULL
OOOOOH!

SHOOM
AAAAAH!

EEEEEM?
FLIP
FLAP

WHAT IS GOING ON IN HERE?!
WE'RE PLAYING WITH OUR NEW MAGIC BEANS!
PIP
POP

MAGIC...BEANS?

MAGIC BEANS! WE BOUGHT 'EM FROM MORTON J. SEASQUIRT!

MORTON J. SEASQUIRT, THE DOOR-TO-DOOR CON ARTIST? YOU WERE RIPPED OFF! THERE'S NO SUCH THING AS MAGIC BEANS!
!!
!!

WHEW! FOR A MINUTE THERE, WE THOUGHT THEY REALLY WERE MAGIC!
THE END

NICKELODEON.
SpongeBob SQUAREPANTS

SPONGEBOB! IT'S ALIEN INVADERS!

IT LOOKS MORE LIKE A TUB OF ICE CREAM...

...BUT IT'S *HUGE!*

WHEEEEEE

BOOM

Vanilla Ice Cream

CREAMBOB CONEPANTS

SOON...
THIS IS THE BEST ICE CREAM DAY EVER!
AS LONG AS ALIENS DON'T SHOW UP.
TOTALLY! IT'S RADICAL!
YEE-HAW!
Vanilla Ice Cream
THESE FOOLS ARE WASTING THIS ICE-CREAM BY EATING IT.
THE ICE CREAM'S FREE, BUT A SPOON'LL COST YE!
KRUSTY SPOONS $5
MEOW.
COME ON, SON. YOU'RE GOING TO GET SICK!

UH-OH.
WHAT?

WE'RE OUT OF ICE CREAM!
WAIT! THERE'S STILL SOME AT THE BOTTOM.

COME ON, PAT! STRETCH!
I'M TRYING, SPONGEBOB!
BUT I'M WORRIED ABOUT--

WHOA!
--FALLING!

AAAAAAAH

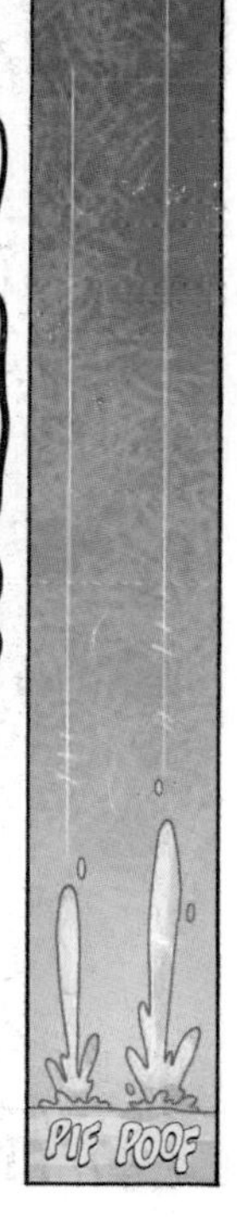
PIF POOF

OOOH... WHERE ARE WE? IT'S SO COLD!
I DON'T KNOW, BUT THE HOUSES HERE LOOK REALLY WEIRD.
THAT ONE LOOKS LIKE AN ICE CREAM TUB!
PINT BOTTOM

WHO LIVES IN A PINT TUB AT THIRTY DEGREES?
CREAMBOB CONEPANTS!
WHO?

CHILLY AND CREAMY AND TASTY IS HE!
CREAMBOB CONEPANTS?
YEAH, THAT'S HIS HOUSE.
DID SOMEONE ASK FOR ME?

CREAMBOB CONEPANTS!
THAT'S ME. YOU GUYS LOOK LOST. WELCOME TO PINT BOTTOM!
I'M SPONGEBOB.
THIS IS MY BEST FRIEND, PATRICK.

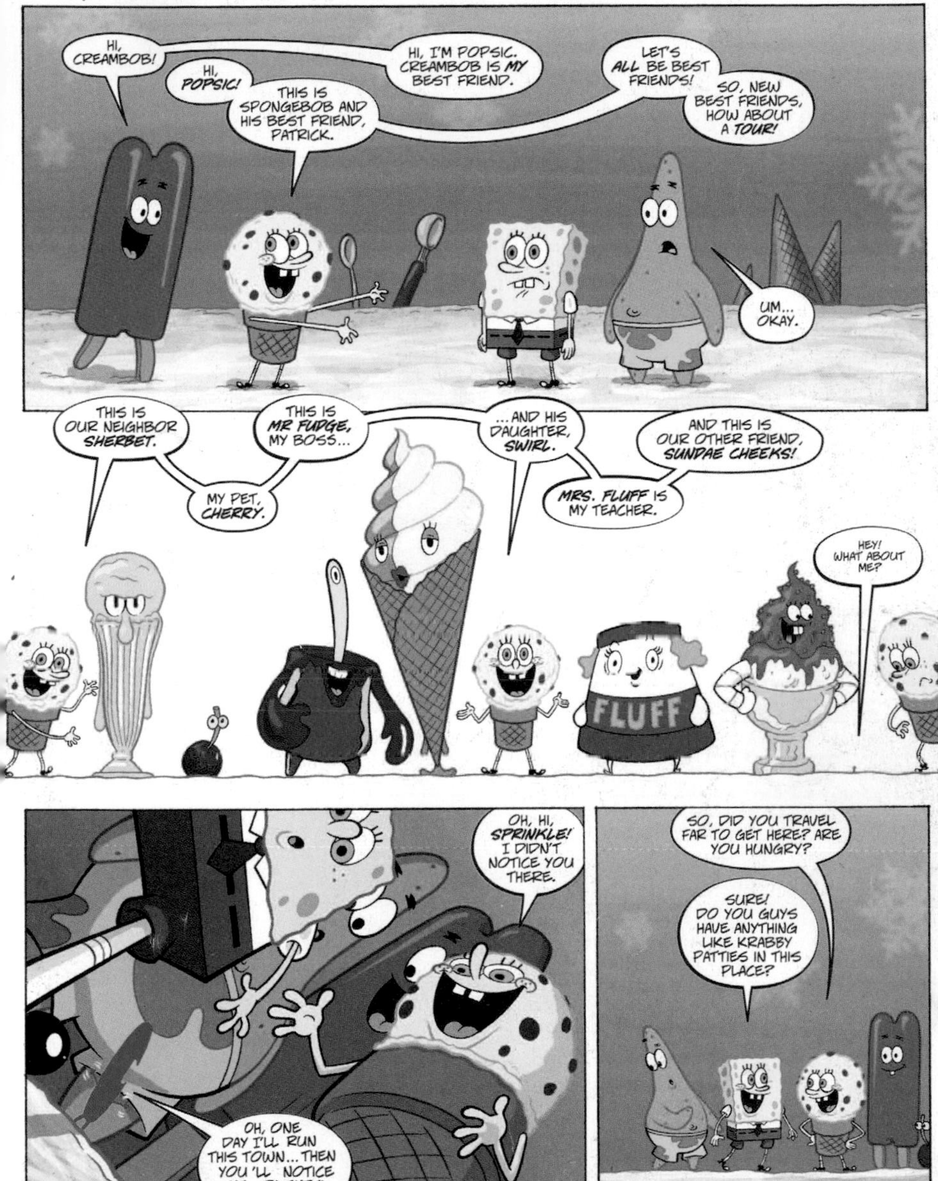

HI, CREAMBOB!
HI, **POPSIC!**
HI, I'M POPSIC. CREAMBOB IS **MY** BEST FRIEND.
THIS IS SPONGEBOB AND HIS BEST FRIEND, PATRICK.
LET'S **ALL** BE BEST FRIENDS!
SO, NEW BEST FRIENDS, HOW ABOUT A **TOUR!**
UM... OKAY.

THIS IS OUR NEIGHBOR **SHERBET.**
MY PET, **CHERRY.**
THIS IS **MR FUDGE,** MY BOSS...
...AND HIS DAUGHTER, **SWIRL.**
MRS. FLUFF IS MY TEACHER.
AND THIS IS OUR OTHER FRIEND, **SUNDAE CHEEKS!**
FLUFF
HEY! WHAT ABOUT ME?

I DON'T KNOW WHAT A KRABBY PATTY IS, BUT HOW ABOUT SOME ICE CREAM CAKE?

OR AN ICE CREAM SANDWICH?

OR YOU CAN CHECK OUT THE *ICE CREAM TRUCK!*
HMM...

LOOKS GOOD.
SHLURP

TASTES *GREAT!*
PATRICK, SHALL WE?
LET'S SHALL!
CLIIIK!

MUNCH
SCOOP
GULP
EAT
SCOOP
SWALLOW
SCOOP

YUM! THAT WAS A GOOD ICE CREAM TRUCK.
THE BEST!
WOW... YOU GUYS MUST BE STUFFED!

HOW ABOUT WE HEAD OVER TO THE GOOBER LAGOON FOR SOME VOLLEYBALL OR SWIMMING...
HEY! WHY ARE YOU LOOKING AT US LIKE THAT? C-COME ON, NOW... AREN'T WE ALL BEST FRIENDS?

BUUUUURRRRP!

WE MIGHT HAVE OVERDONE IT.

SPONGEBOB! PATRICK! Y'ALL DOWN THERE?

WHAT THE HECK? Y'ALL LOOK LIKE YOU ATE AN... **EVERYTHING!!**
COME ON, BOYS, LIFT YER BLUBBER UP OUTTA THERE!
WE'RE... COMING... HUFF... HUFF... HANG... ON...

SOON...
LET'S GO, FELLAS! THE WEIGHT AIN'T GONNA LOSE ITSELF!
HUFF
PUFF

LATER...
PHEW! THAT WORKOUT MADE ME HUNGRY FOR MORE ICE CREAM.

ME TOO.

HRM.

LICK
THE END

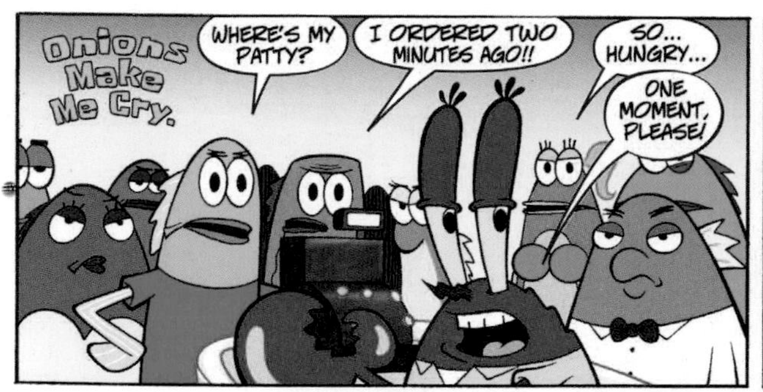
Onions Make Me Cry.
WHERE'S MY PATTY?
I ORDERED TWO MINUTES AGO!!
SO... HUNGRY...
ONE MOMENT, PLEASE!

SPONGEBOB!! WHAT ARE YOU DOING BACK THERE?

CREEK
M--MR. KRABS...?
YES?

THE ONIONS ARE MAKING ME CRY!

ONIONS? WHAT? WHY ME??

HERE, YOU MAN THE REGISTER. I'LL TAKE CARE OF THE ONIONS!
SNIFF SNIFF
WIPE

GOOD LUCK IN THERE, MR. KRABS!
HMPH!

HEY, DON'T WORRY! MR. KRABS HAS EVERYTHING UNDER CON--

BWAHH-HAWW-HAW!
SWING

OH, NO! THE ONIONS MADE YOU CRY, TOO, MR. KRABS?

NO, NO... I... JUST HAVE SOMETHING... CAUGHT IN... IN MY...

WAAAHHHH!
SQUEEZE

OH, BROTHER!

WELL... MAYBE IT IS A BIT MUCH...

ARE YEH READY TO GO IN THERE, SPONGEBOB?
UM... I GUESS SO...
THEN LET'S BE BRAVE TOGETHER!

CREEK

WELL, WELL, WELL, IF IT AIN'T BUG-EYES AND SQUISHY-HEAD!
YOU KEEP FRESH IN THAT SHELL?!
NICE HOLES!
END

WAITING...
SPECIAL OFFER

ALL RIGHT! I CAN'T WAIT!
SPECIAL OFFER

GOOD MORNING, SPONGEBOB! GOT A LETTER FOR ME?
SURE DO! HERE!

OKEY DOKE! AND HERE'S YOUR MAIL!
OH, BOY, OH, BOY!

HMM... YOU WOULDN'T HAPPEN TO HAVE A PACKAGE FOR ME, WOULD YOU? I SENT AWAY FOR IT A LONG TIME AGO!

YOU MEAN THIS?? BUT I HAVEN'T EVEN LEFT YET!

OH, YEAH! SILLY ME! WELL, I'LL SEE YOU TOMORROW!
SEE YA!

'MORNING! IS THERE A PACKAGE?
SORRY, SPONGEBOB.

PACKAGE TODAY??
NOPE, NOT TODAY!

PACKAGE?? PACKAGE??
N-NN-NO! P-PACKAGE!
SHAKE SHAKE

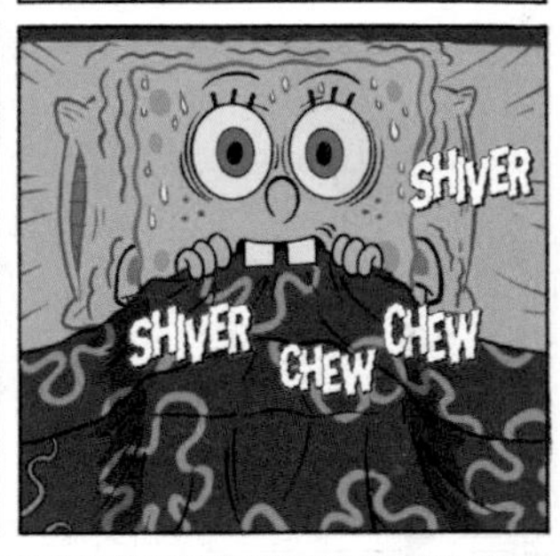
SHIVER
SHIVER
CHEW
CHEW

OH, SPONNNGEBOB!!

GASP
IT'S HERE!!

THANK YOU, THANK YOU, THANK YOU!! I'VE BEEN WAITING FOREVER! I THOUGHT THIS WOULD NEVER COME!!
ENJOY IT, BUDDY!

TEAR
SHRED

AW, MAN...!
I ALREADY KNOW MOST OF THIS STUFF!
HOW TO BE PATIENT
END

BRITE BITE
SON, I KNOW YER SCUPPERED AFTER TWELVE HOURS OF FLIPPIN' PATTIES, BUT ME CUSTOMERS PREFER THEIR SERVICE WITH A SMILE.
I'LL WORK ON IT, MR. KRABS...

EVERYONE LOVES A SHINY GRIN! MAKE THAT SO-SO SMILE SO, SO FANTASTIC!
WOW! IT'S LIKE HE READ MY MIND!

IMPROVE YOUR LIFE WITH BRITE BITE...
...THE FASTER BITE BRIGHTENER!

LOOK OUT, PATRICK!
SMOP
HI, SPONGEBOB!

GIVE ME ALL YOUR BRITE BITE, PLEASE!

IF ONE IS GOOD, EIGHTY-SIX MUST BE GREAT! RIGHT, GARY?

48 HOURS LATER...
I FEEL THE BRIGHTENING POWER!

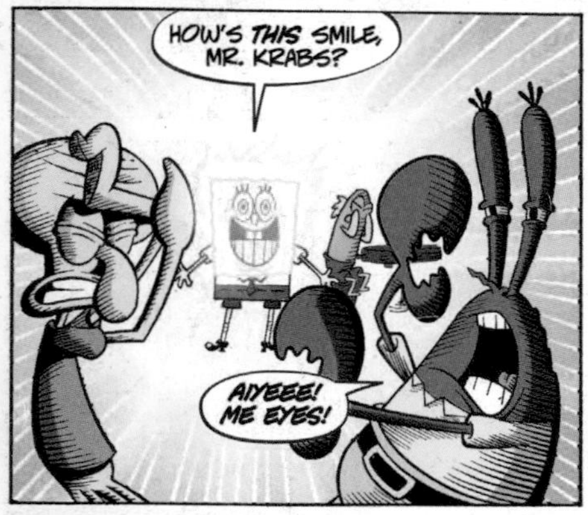
HOW'S THIS SMILE, MR. KRABS?
AIYEEE! ME EYES!

YEH BEST SHOVE OFF, SON! THEM TEETH'RE BAD FOR BUSINESS!
BUT... BUT... AW!

BUT SOON...
WILL YA LOOK AT THAT GARGANTUAN GLOW!
SAY, I CAN USE A BRIGHT LAD LIKE YOU!

KEEP ON SMILIN', MATEY!
REPLACEMENT BULBS ARE PRICEY!
THE END

HAPPY BIRTHDAYS!
HAPPY BIRTHDAY, SPONGEBOB!!!
HUH?!

I FIGURED YOU CAN NEVER HAVE TOO MANY ROCKS!
ER... THANKS, PATRICK, BUT--
YOU'RE WELCOME!

...SO WHEN PATRICK TOLD ME IT WAS YOUR BIRTHDAY, I KNEW WE HAD TO CELEBRATE! HAPPY BIRTHDAY!
THANKS, SANDY!

HAPPY BIRTHDAY, SON!
AN' WHEN YER DONE READIN' YER CARD, PUT IT BACK IN THE NAPKIN DISPENSER.
OKAY, MR. KRABS!

WELCOME TO THE CHUM BUCKET'S "ALL YOU CAN EAT BIRTHDAY BUFFET!"
IT'S THE ONLY WAY I'LL EVER GET RID OF THIS SLOP.
UM, THANKS, PLANKTON.

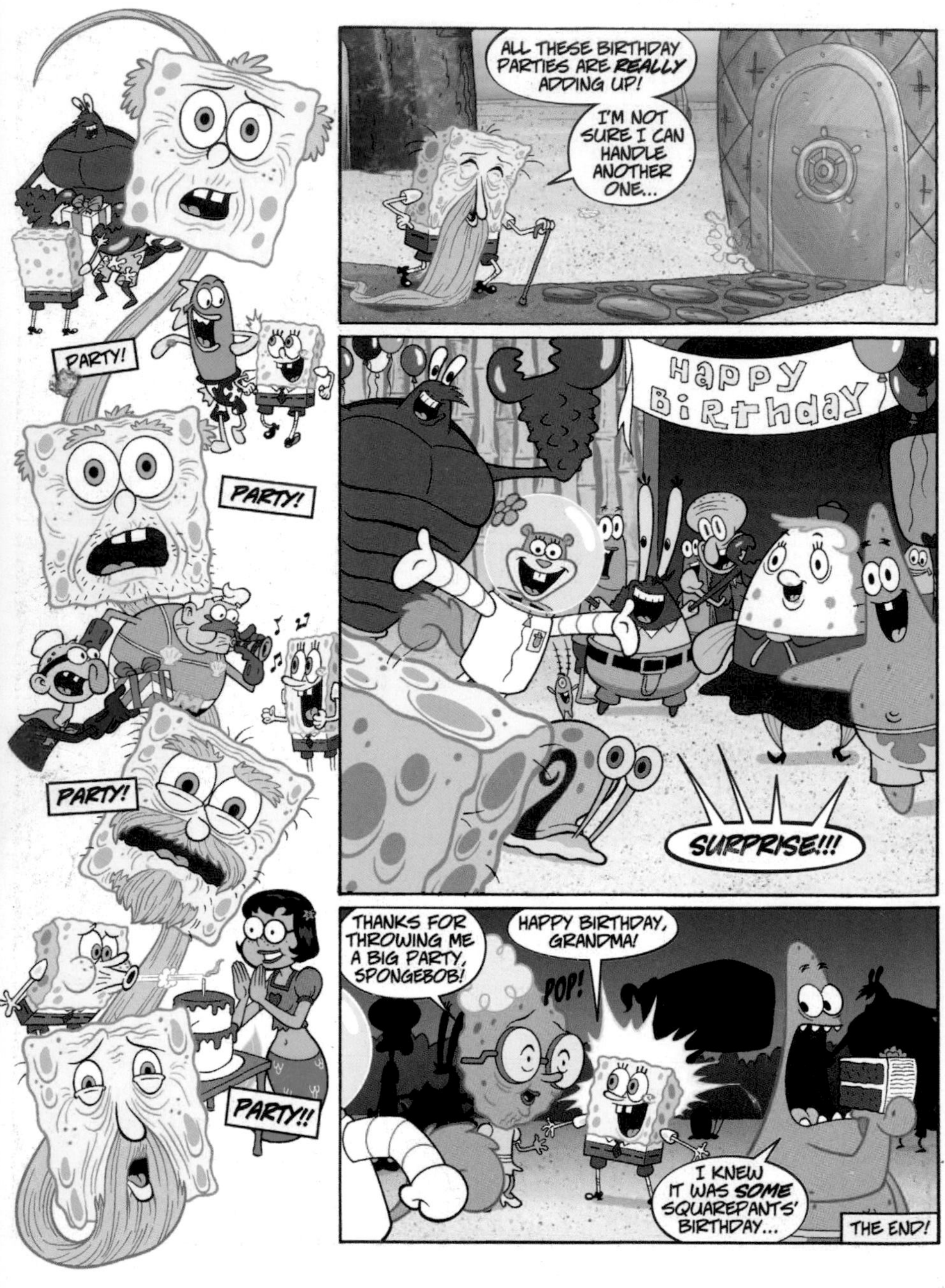
PARTY!
PARTY!
PARTY!
PARTY!!
ALL THESE BIRTHDAY PARTIES ARE REALLY ADDING UP!
I'M NOT SURE I CAN HANDLE ANOTHER ONE...
HAPPY BIRTHDAY
SURPRISE!!!
THANKS FOR THROWING ME A BIG PARTY, SPONGEBOB!
HAPPY BIRTHDAY, GRANDMA!
POP!
I KNEW IT WAS SOME SQUAREPANTS' BIRTHDAY...
THE END!

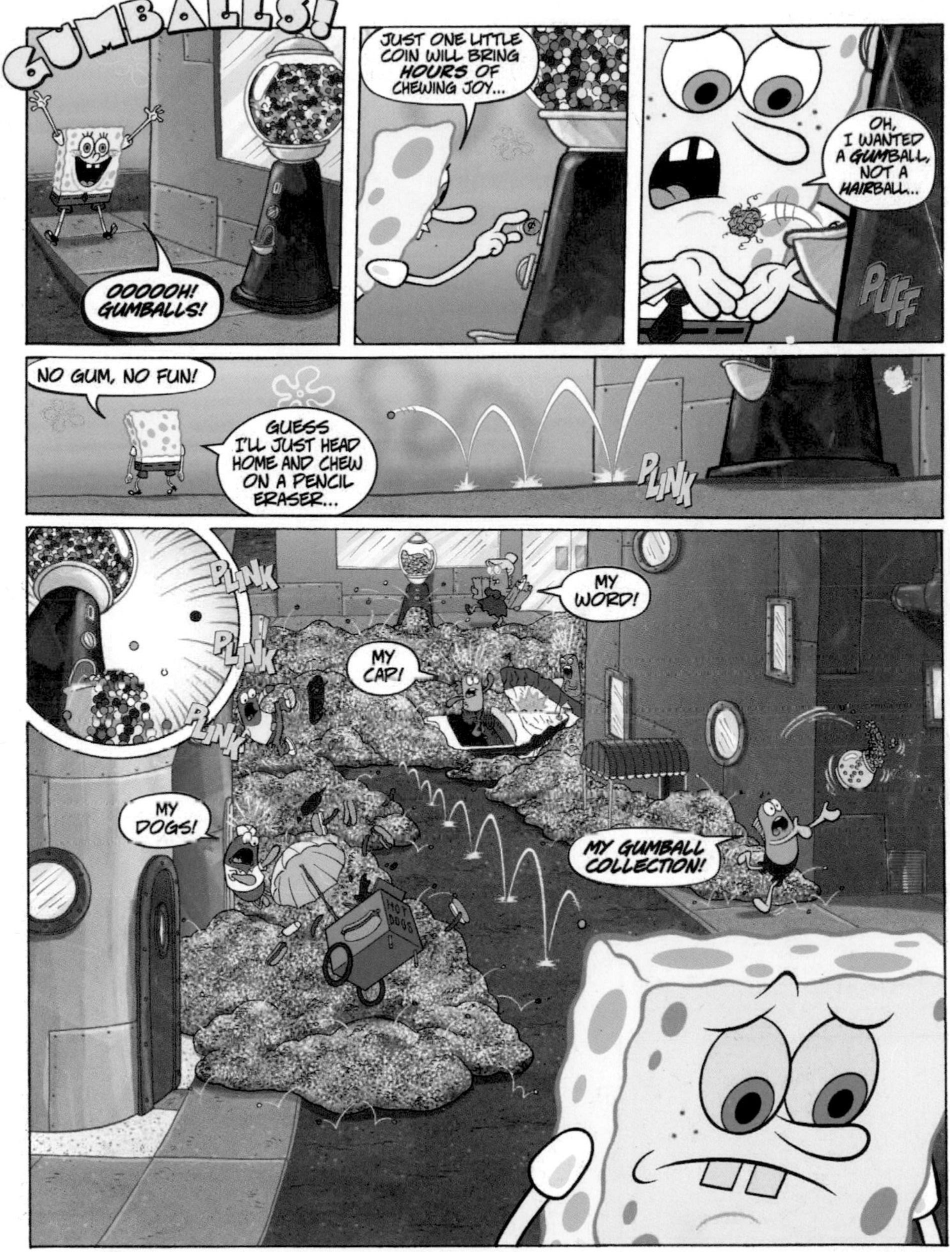

GUMBALLS!
OOOOOOH! GUMBALLS!

JUST ONE LITTLE COIN WILL BRING HOURS OF CHEWING JOY...

OH, I WANTED A GUMBALL, NOT A HAIRBALL...
PUFF

NO GUM, NO FUN!
GUESS I'LL JUST HEAD HOME AND CHEW ON A PENCIL ERASER...
PLINK

PLINK
PLINK
PLINK
MY WORD!
MY CAP!
MY DOGS!
MY GUMBALL COLLECTION!

TOMORROW'S FORECAST: CANDY CANES WITH THE POSSIBILITY OF...UM... CHOCOLATE?!
HMM... NEEDS KETCHUP!
BOUNCE
BOUNCE

THIS ERASER TASTED BETTER WHEN IT WAS NEW.
BOUNCE

YAY!! OH DEAR, DELICIOUS GUMBALL, HOW DID YOU EVER FIND--

EWWW, I DON'T LIKE THE GREEN ONES!
PLINK
END

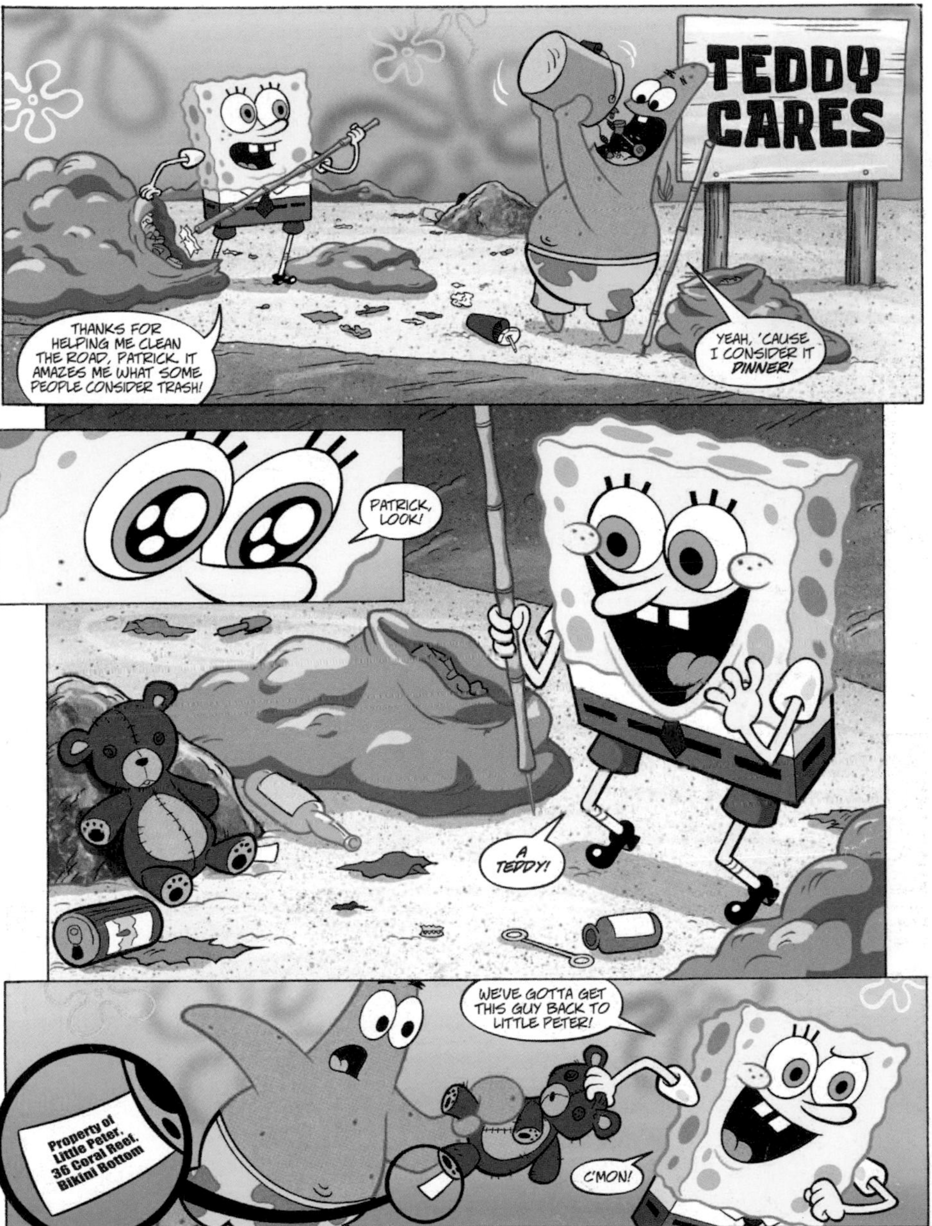

PATRICK, LOOK!

A TEDDY!

AND ALONG THE WAY...
TEDDY, THIS IS THE KRUSTY KRAB...
MY HUMBLE ABODE...
AND JELLYFISH FIELDS!
HOW I WISH I COULD SHOW YOU MORE!

BUT WE'RE HERE. HOME SWEET HOME...
WHEW!
LITTLE PETER

IS LITTLE PETER HERE?
I'M LITTLE PETER.

THEN I BELIEVE THIS IS YOURS...

OH, THANK YOU, YOUNG MAN!
HOW AM I SUPPOSED TO LIVE WITHOUT TEDDY?

BURRRRRP
PATRICK! HE'S BEAUTIFUL! I'LL LOVE HIM FOREVER AND EVER.
GOT ANYTHING TO EAT?
END

SpongeBob: The Mini-Comic

STORY BY: CHRIS DUFFY PENCILS BY: GREGG SCHIGIEL INKS BY: JEFF ALBRECHT
COLOR BY: WES DZIOBA LETTERING BY: COMICRAFT

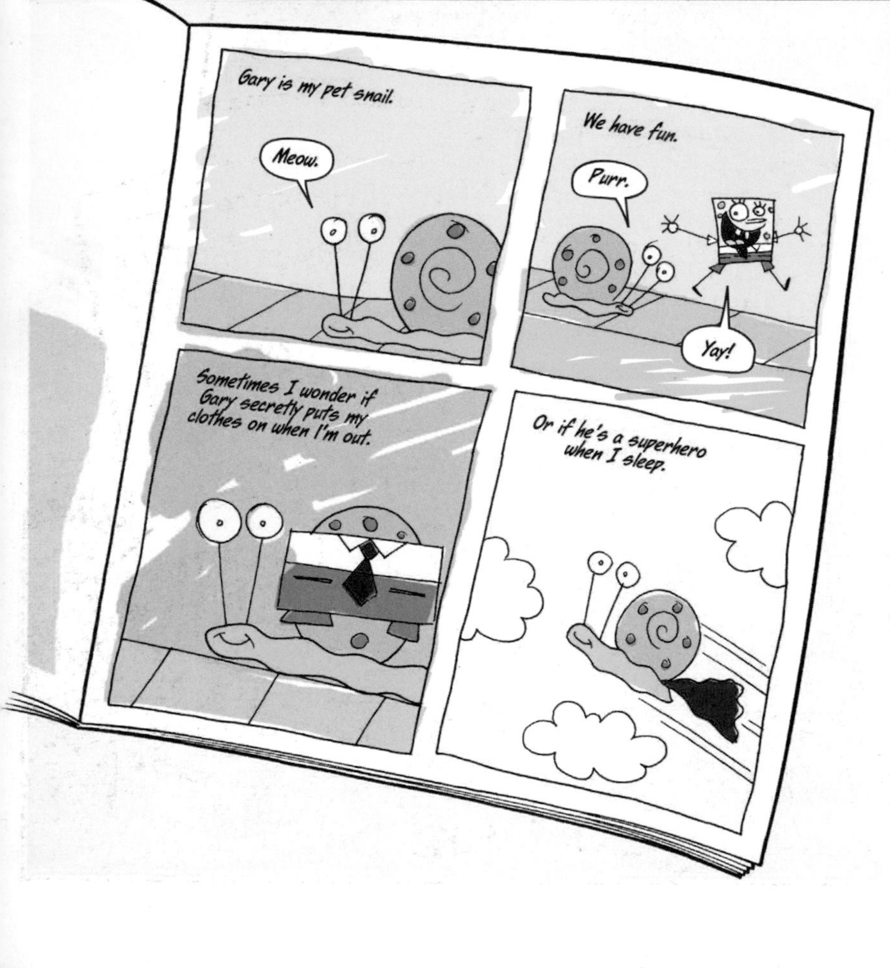

Gary is my pet snail.

Meow.

We have fun.

Purr.

Yay!

Sometimes I wonder if Gary secretly puts my clothes on when I'm out.

Or if he's a superhero when I sleep.

I also wonder...what if Gary wore a hat?
?
And what if he had legs like mine?
But I like him just like he is -- my pal!
THE END
YOU LIKE IT!
PURR PURR
YAY!
WHO LIKES WHAT?

MY COMIC, PATRICK! GARY LIKES IT. WANT A COPY?
COMICS, EH? LOW-BROW STUFF!
PURR
GARY

I SUPPOSE THIS IS ALL RIGHT-- IF YOU GO FOR THIS KIND OF THING.
GARY
DO YOU HAVE ANYTHING TO EAT?

LATER...
HI, MR. KRABS. I'M HERE FOR WORK!
WANT TO SEE A COMIC I MADE?
A FUNNY BOOK, EH?
GARY

HMM...

I HOPE HE DOESN'T FIRE YOU FOR SHOWING HIM SUCH BABY JUNK!
WHAT?!?

HAR! HAR! HAR!
HERE, SQUIDWARD--LOOKIT GARY WITH A HAT!
IT IS MILDLY AMUSING. IN A MORONIC KIND OF WAY.
GARY

WOW... SQUIDWARD LOVES MY COMIC!

MOMMY, I WANT A COMIC, TOO!
HMM?
GARY
COMIC$ COMIC$

SOON...
A SNAIL... WITH A HAT!
NOW I'VE SEEN EVERYTHING!
HA HAH HO!
COMICS
$1.00

WOW-- THIS IS FUN!
YEAH-- EVERYBODY LOVES MY COMIC!
IT IS?
THEY DO?

WATCH OUT.
BUMP

ARE YOU GONNA DRAW A COMIC, PATRICK?
QUIET.
I'M COMICKING.
IT'S FUN.
EVERYONE WILL LOVE IT.

WHAT'S IT ABOUT?
SHH!

CAN I SEE?
ARGH

SCRIBBLE
FINISHED?

SCRAWL
SCRATCH
OOGA BOOGA!

HERE!
FLOP
CO MI CK
WOW!
Fun comick
Whate it about ?
Shhhhh
comick
pencille
comick
ARG
Can I see ?

FINISHED
OOOGA?
BOOGA
pensil
everyone will Love now
comick Book
THE
END
COMICS
$1.00
DOES... EVERYONE... LOVE IT?
UM...
SPONGEBOB...?
WHAT THE HECK IS THAT?
SCRIBBLE
SCRAWL
HA!
NOW I'VE SEEN EVERYTHING!
SPONGEBOB...?
DO THEY LOVE IT?
YES!
END

EXTRA POINTS
SPONGEBOB! QUICK! OPEN THE DOOR! HELP!
KNOCK! KNOCK! KNOCK!
COMING, PATRICK!

I LOST BOTH MY ARMS! LEFTY AND NOT-LEFTY!

HOW DID THIS HAPPEN?

THAT'S KINDA PERSONAL, SPONGEBOB. ALL I CAN SAY IS, LIVING UNDER A HUGE ROCK HAS ITS DANGERS.

DON'T WORRY, PATRICK. SEA STARS CAN EASILY GROW THEIR ARMS BACK!
WHAT'S THAT GOT TO DO WITH IT?

YOU'RE A SEA STAR!
OH, YEAH!

NNNGGGHHHH...
YOU CAN DO IT...

I DID IT!
POP

THERE YOU GO, PATRICK! JUST KEEP AT IT!
RIGHT! THANKS, SPONGEBOB!

SPONGEBOB!
HUH?

I THINK I GOT CARRIED AWAY.
END

GUMMY
CHEW! CHEW!
CHEW!
CHEW!

PAF! POK!

CHEW!
CHEW!
CHEW!

CHEW!
CHEW!
CHEW!
CHEW!

CHEW!
CHEW!
CHEW!
CHEW!

CHEW! CHEW!
CHEW!
CHEW!

CHEW!
CHEW!

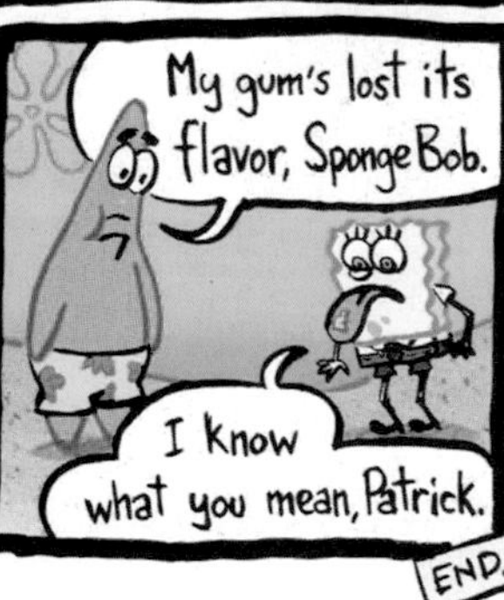
My gum's lost its flavor, SpongeBob.
I know what you mean, Patrick.
END.

SPONGEBOB'S PET SNAIL, GARY

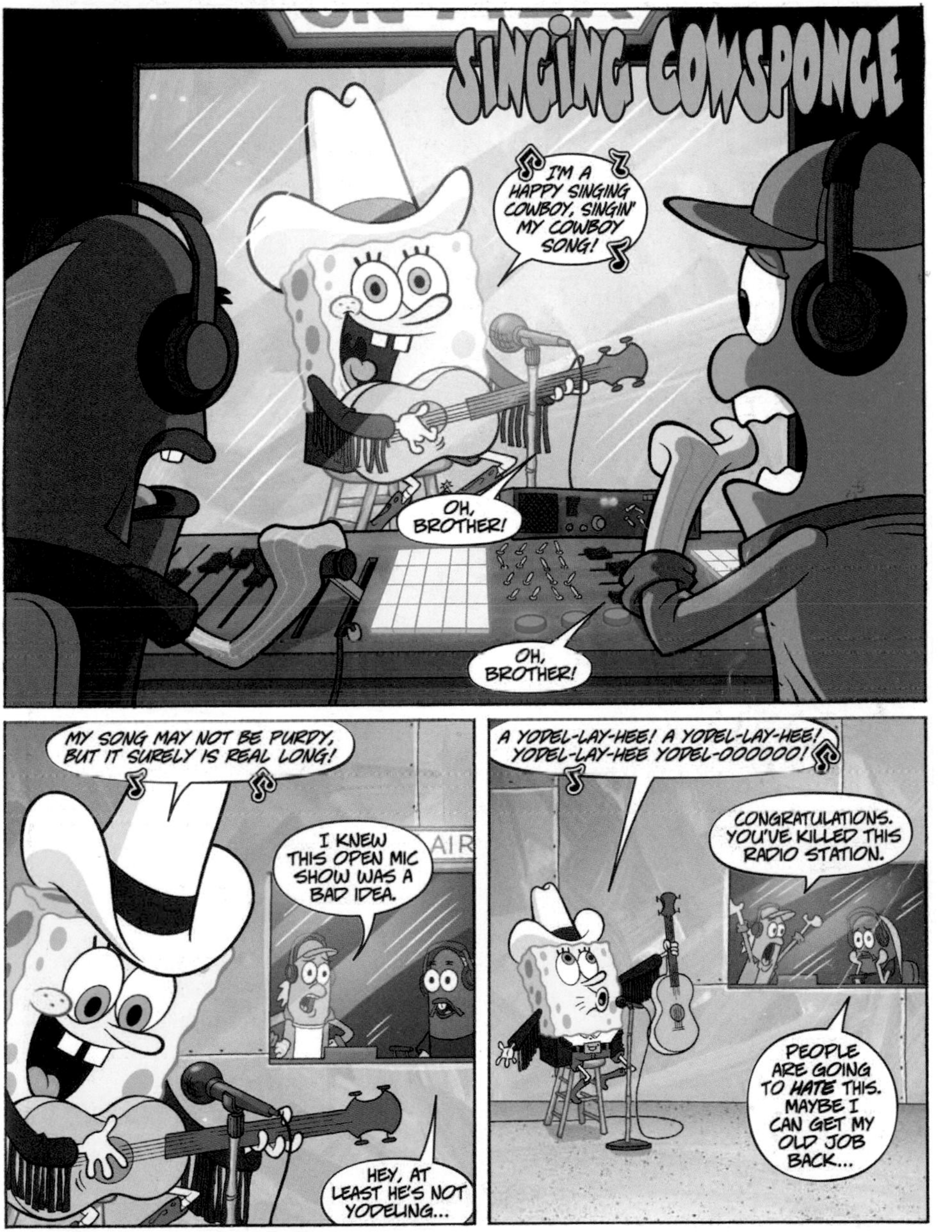

SINGING COWSPONGE

I'M A HAPPY SINGING COWBOY, SINGIN' MY COWBOY SONG!

OH, BROTHER!

OH, BROTHER!

YODEL-LAY-HEEEE
I LIKE THIS BECAUSE IT REMINDS ME OF THE TUNES OF YESTERYEAR.
YODEL-LAY-HEEEEEEE
I LIKE THIS 'CAUSE IT REMINDS ME OF TEXAS!
YODEL-LAY-HEE-HOOOOOOO!
I LIKE THIS BECAUSE IT REMINDS ME OF PEOPLE BEING TORTURED!
OKAY, THAT'S ENOUGH! I'LL TOSS HIM OUT!
WAIT! PEOPLE LIKE IT! WE'D BETTER LET HIM FINISH HIS SONG!
WOO-WOO-HOO...

MANY VERSES LATER...
THIS COWBOY'LL SING 'BOUT EVERY SEA COW HE'S KNOWN...
ARE YOU SURE PEOPLE LIKE THIS?
THAT'S WHAT THEY SAID ON THE PHONE... THREE HOURS AGO.
ENOUGH! MAKE IT STOP!
THERE'S FLOSSIE 'N BOSSIE...
ELSIE MAE 'N BABETTE... BROWNIE 'N CLOWNIE...
THIS SONG IS LASTIN' LONGER THAN THE DROUGHT OF '95!
AN' SOME OTHER ONES I FERGET...
THIS DOESN'T SOUND LIKE TORTURE!
THIS IS TORTURE!
MUST... DESTROY... SINGER!

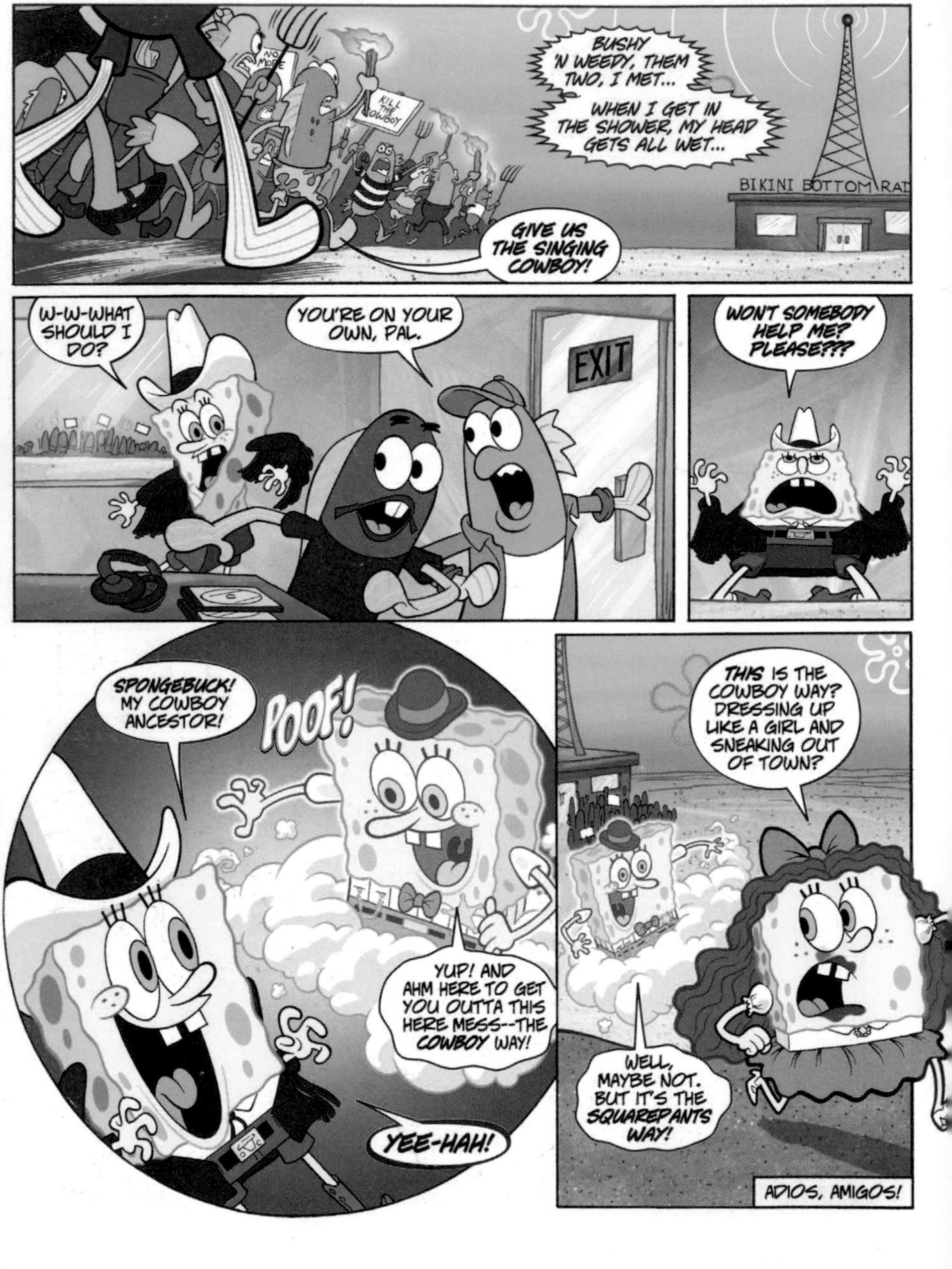

SPONGEBUCK! MY COWBOY ANCESTOR!

POOF!

YUP! AND AHM HERE TO GET YOU OUTTA THIS HERE MESS--THE *COWBOY* WAY!

YEE-HAH!

THIS IS THE COWBOY WAY? DRESSING UP LIKE A GIRL AND SNEAKING OUT OF TOWN?

WELL, MAYBE NOT. BUT IT'S THE ***SQUAREPANTS*** WAY!

ADIOS, AMIGOS!

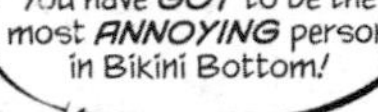

Ree-eee-eek-kkk

That's NOTHING! THIS is REALLY annoying!

I'm not touching you... I'm not touching you...

THAT all ya got?? I can beat that nine ways to SUNDAY!

HOURS PASS...

Say... did you ALWAYS have that mole?

floo-floo floo!

Smell my BREATH!!

Whatcha doin'? Whatcha doin'? Whatcha doin'?

Snort! Hyuck! Snort! Snort! Snort! Hyuck!

SLAP!

Whatcha doin'?

Nails on a BLACK-BOARD!
Lickin' SUEDE!
THAT'S IT! Put me out of my MISERY!
You two are the most ANNOYING people who ever LIVED!
It's a TIE! It's a TIE!
ACTUALLY, Squidward, that's not a TIE--
--it's a SCREW-DRIVER.
A SCREW-DRIVER?!
Patrick, you must be the STUPIDEST person in BIKINI BOTTOM.
NO! I AM!
ME, TOO!
YAAH!
ME am the NOT SMARTEST with having some of the BRAINS!
2 + 2 = BACON!
Get AWAY from me!
WAAH! I'm never bestest at ANYTHING!
Duh End!

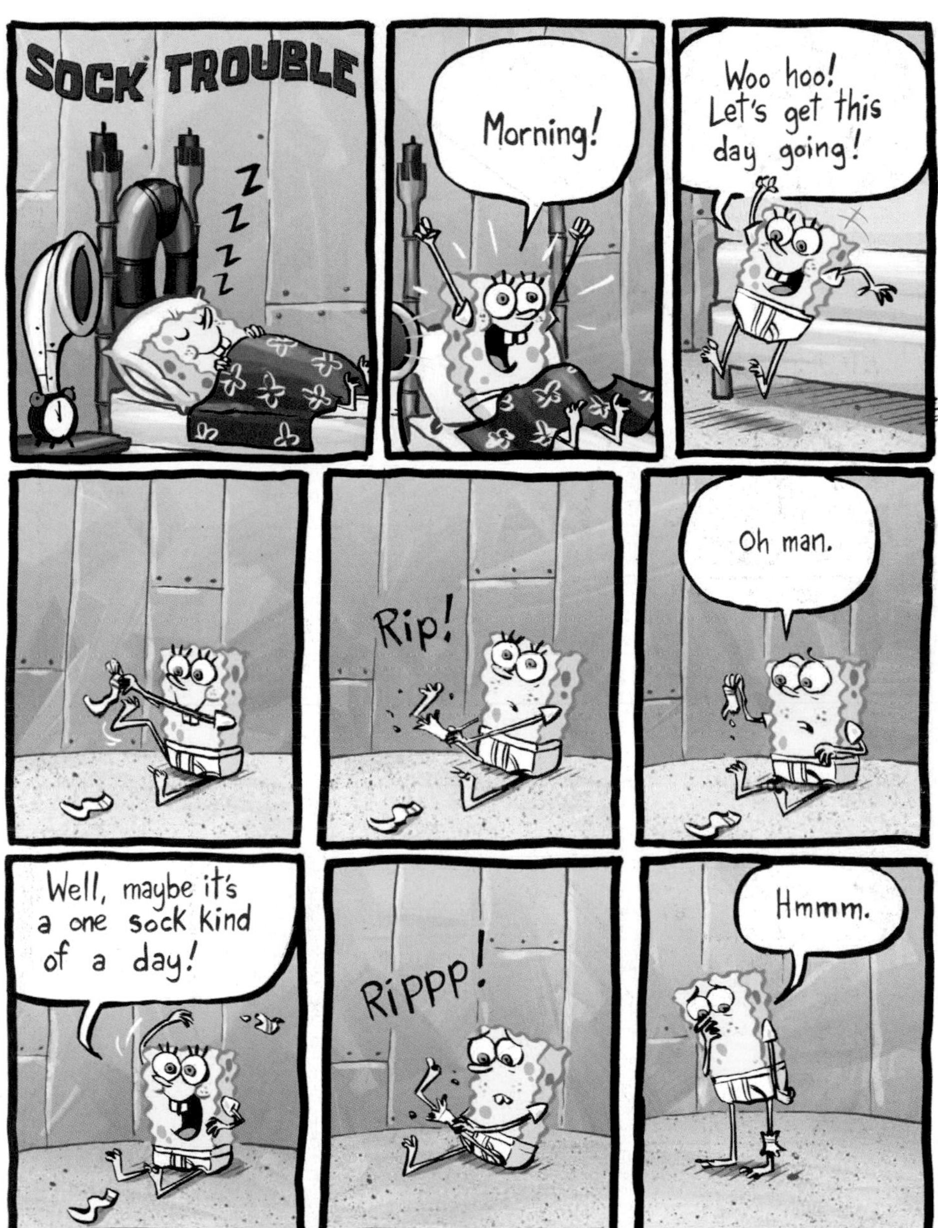
SOCK TROUBLE
Z Z Z Z
Morning!
Woo hoo! Let's get this day going!
Rip!
Oh man.
Well, maybe it's a one sock kind of a day!
Rippp!
Hmmm.

Guess I'll just find another pair in the sock drawer.

SHOOP!

Sea moths!

All my socks... gone!

What am I gonna do?

Later...
Whoa! SpongeBob?

Hey Patrick! Who needs socks when you've got MOTH POWER!
END.

Packing
LOOK AT THIS, GARY!
GRANDMA'S INVITED ME TO SPEND THE NIGHT AT HER HOUSE!
YAY!

GOTTA TAKE EXTRA CLOTHES--MAKING COOKIES CAN GET PRETTY MESSY!

MY ALARM CLOCK'LL MAKE SURE I WAKE UP EXTRA EARLY! HMM, I THINK I NEED A BIGGER CASE...

SOMETIMES THE PICTURE ON GRANDMA'S TV IS A LITTLE FUZZY...

THIS TRUNK ISN'T BIG ENOUGH, EITHER!

CAN'T GO TO GRANDMA'S WITHOUT *YOU*, GARY!
BUT WAIT-- WHAT ABOUT MY OTHER FRIENDS?

LATER...
WHEE! I'M LUGGAGE!
SPONGEBOB, LET US OUT!
BUT THEN I WON'T GET THE THREE BUCKS HE PROMISED ME!

TARTAR SAUCE. I'LL NEVER BE ABLE TO DECIDE WHAT TO PACK.
DOES THIS MEAN I'M NOT LUGGAGE ANYMORE?

SO YOU'LL COME OVER *HERE* INSTEAD, GRANDMA?
THAT'S *GREAT*!

HI, SWEETIE!
I HOPE YOU DON'T MIND. I HAD A LITTLE TROUBLE DECIDING WHAT TO PACK...
THE END

BATTLE MONSTERS
WRITTEN BY DAVID LEWMAN PENCILS BY GREGG SCHIGIEL
INKS BY JEFF ALBRECHT COLOR BY WES DZIBOA
LETTERING BY COMICRAFT
HEY, SPONGEBOB! LET'S PLAY!
I'M ALREADY PLAYING, PATRICK
WHAT ARE YOU PLAYING? "GLOVES AND DUSTERS"?
ONLY THE MOST FUN GAME EVER-- BATTLE MONSTER CARDS!
HOW DO YOU PLAY?
I TAKE A CARD OUT, DUST IT, AND PUT IT BACK!
AND YOU GET TO WATCH!
WHEE.

WOW, YOU MUST HAVE EVERY BUTT MONSTER EVER BORN!
BATTLE MONSTER. ALL BUT ONE...

I'VE TRIED FOR YEARS...
...BUT I COULD NEVER GET MY HANDS ON FLIPTAIL!
HE'S THE RAREST OF ALL!

YOU KNOW, PATRICK, YOU REALLY SHOULD COLLECT SOMETHING. COLLECTING IS GREAT!
I HAVE A COLLECTION...

OH, YEAH? WHAT DO YOU COLLECT?
UM... BATTLE MONSTERS!

BATTLE MONSTERS?!
YEAH! I'LL SHOW YOU MY FAVORITE...

...LINTY!
LINTY'S NOT A REAL BATTLE MONSTER, PATRICK.
HE IS SO!

COME ON, LINTY, LET'S GO CATCH FLOPTAIL!
FLIPTAIL!
YEAH, THAT ONE!

THE NEXT MORNING...
OH, SPONGEBOB! I'VE GOT SOMETHING TO SHOW YOU!!!
COMING, PATRICK...

FLIPTAIL!
TOLD YOU I'D CATCH HIM.
MURP!

THE REAL FLIPTAIL! WHERE'D YOU FIND HIM?
COME ON! I'LL SHOW YOU!

THIS IS IT.
LOOK AT ALL THE BATTLE MONSTERS!
GLARG!
GROOBLE!
HRNK?

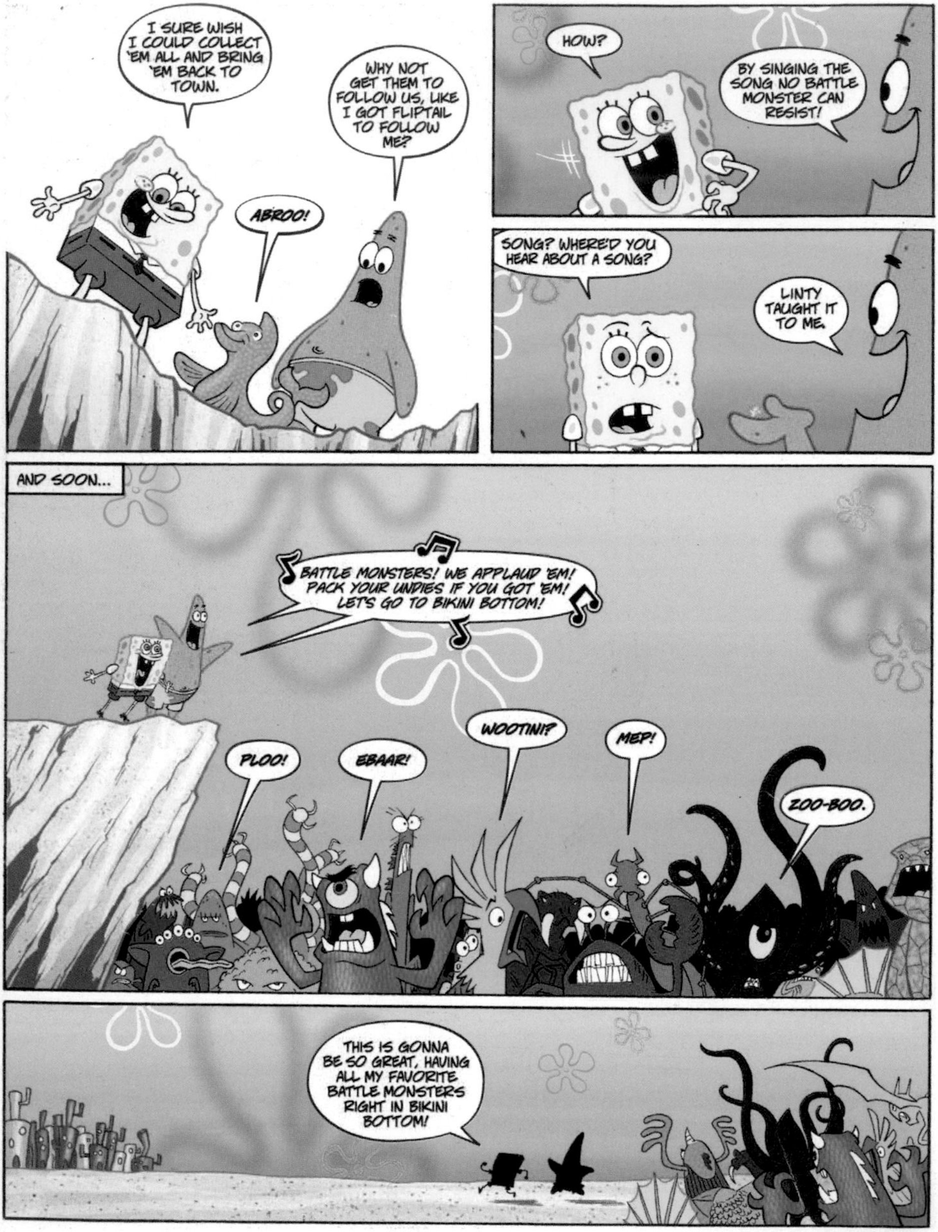

AND SOON...

BATTLE MONSTERS! WE APPLAUD 'EM! PACK YOUR UNDIES IF YOU GOT 'EM! LET'S GO TO BIKINI BOTTOM!

PLOO!

EBAAR!

WOOTINI?

MEP!

ZOO-BOO.

HEY, GUYS! WHERE YOU GOING?
GREEPP!
ICE CREAM!
FLURBY-FLUM ICE CREAM!

AW, THEY WANT ICE CREAM. ISN'T THAT CUTE?
I WANT FLURBY-FLUM ICE CREAM.
GOOFY GOOBERS

ZIBBLE!
MARF!
TWO ICE CREAMS, PLEASE.
WE'RE CLOSED!
FISH PASTE.

HMM... MAYBE BRINGING THE BATTLE MONSTERS TO TOWN WASN'T SUCH A GREAT IDEA.
WHAT MAKES YOU THINK SO?

CHOMP
GARSH!
NOW CAN I DRIVE, MRS. PUFF?
CLASS IS CANCELED!

GUESS WE WON'T BE VISITING THE FRY COOK MUSEUM TODAY.
BUT IT'S "DRESS LIKE A FRY COOK AND GET IN FREE DAY!"
FRY COOK MUSEUM
FRIM!
FRAM!

BUT SQUIDWARD, I DON'T KNOW HOW TO MAKE A WUMBY PATTY!!
KROOGIE FRIES WIT DAT!

LOOKS LIKE THE BATTLE MONSTERS HAVE CHASED ALL THE JELLYFISH AWAY.
BARNACLES.

ALL THE GOOD SPOTS ARE TAKEN!
ALL THE BAD SPOTS, TOO.

BaRG'N-
AT LEAST WE CAN CHEER OURSELVES UP WITH A LITTLE BUBBLE-BLOWING!
YAY! BUBBLES!

BUBBLES
YOU'RE SOLD OUT?!
YUP. THAT GUY JUST BOUGHT THE LAST BOTTLE.
GRUBBLE BUBBLES! TOOT!

BaRG'N-MaRT
THAT'S THE LAST SEAWEED!
THESE BATTLE MONSTERS HAVE GOT TO GO!

NOW HEAR THIS! ALL BATTLE MONSTERS MUST GO BACK TO THEIR CANYON IMMEDIATELY!
BUTT MONSTERS GO HOME
GRONK?! SAYS WHO-WHO?

SAYS...UM...ME-ME, SPONGEBOB! YOU MUST DO AS I SAY, FOR I AM...ER...SUPREME BATTLE MONSTER MASTER!
SNERP! SNAPP!
PAA! WHAT MAKE YOU MASTER KLOOBIE?

MY COLLECTION MAKES ME YOUR MASTER! TAKE ME TO MY HOUSE AND I'LL SHOW YOU!
BATTLE MONSTERS! WE APPLAUD 'EM! PACK YOUR UNDIES -
ZUMP! WE NOT LIKE THAT BERFY SONG NO MORE!

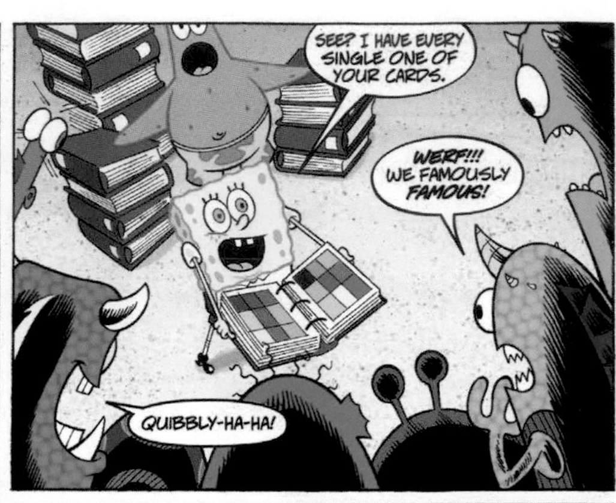

SEE? I HAVE EVERY SINGLE ONE OF YOUR CARDS.
WERF!!! WE FAMOUSLY FAMOUS!
QUIBBLY-HA-HA!

YERTZ! THIS TOWN TOO SMALL FOR CELEBRITIES LIKE US!
WE GO NOOBIE-NOW TO SHELL CITY! LURP!
SHELL C
GOODBY--UM...LURP!

I MISS THEM ALREADY...
THAT'S A RELIEF.
I GUESS...
HEY, LINTY! YOU DECIDED TO STAY! YAY!
I'M YOU-YOU'S FRIENDY-FRIEND, PATRICK! YERPS!
?!
LURP!

The Sleepover
BOY, SPONGEBOB! THIS SLEEPOVER AT YOUR HOUSE IS THE GREATEST IDEA EVER!
GLAD YOU THINK SO, BUDDY! COME ON, LET'S HIT THE HAY.
COOKIE WAFERS
ICE CREAM
MERMAID MAN

AND NOW LET'S GO TO SLEEP!
WHOMP
WHACK!

GEE, YOUR TOOTHPASTE TASTES FUNNY.
THAT'S 'CAUSE YOU'RE USING MY SHAMPOO!

YOUR TOWEL FEELS WEIRD.
PATRICK, THAT'S THE SHOWER CURTAIN!

MAN, YOU CAN REALLY SMELL THE PINEAPPLE AT NIGHT--AND THIS PILLOW TASTES BIZARRE.
YOU'RE NOT SUPPOSED TO EAT IT.

HOW COME YOU GET THREE MATTRESSES, AND I HAVE TO SLEEP ON THE FLOOR?
YOU'RE RIGHT!
AS THE GUEST, YOU SHOULD GET THE BED.

COMFY NOW?
NOPE.

NOW?
NOPE.

NOW?
NOPE.

I DON'T GET IT.
WE STARFISH ARE EXCELLENT SLEEPERS. I'VE PERSONALLY WON MANY PROFESSIONAL COMPETITIONS.
I'VE GOT IT!

SLEEP WELL, MY FRIEND!
ZZZZZ...
THE END

HEY, SANDY...
WHAT'S A CHICKEN?
A CHICKEN...?

WELL, ON THE ONE HAND, IT'S A BIRD, BUT IT--
WHAT'S A BIRD?

Y'KNOW, ONE OF THEM FLYIN' CRITTERS.
LIKE A JELLYFISH?

NO, SILLY! BIRDS HAVE WINGS AN' FEATHERS ON 'EM.
WHAT'S WINGS?
AND WHAT ARE FEATHERS?

WINGS... WINGS ARE LIKE ARMS, KINDA, BUT BIRDS FLAP 'EM...

AN' THEY'RE COVERED IN FEATHERS. THOSE HELP 'EM FLY, 'CEPT CHICKENS DON'T FLY MUCH.

AN' FEATHERS. FEATHERS ARE THEM THINGS Y'ALL STUFF PILLOWS WITH.

MANY HOURS LATER...
TIME FOR ME NAP!
EH?
?
WHAT'D THEM BOYS DO WITH MY PILLOWS?
CHICKEN! CHICKEN!
I'M A BIRD, WATCH ME FLY! CHICKEN!
WHAT ARE THOSE NITWITS UP TO NOW?
I THINK THEY'RE PRETENDIN' TO BE CHICKENS.
WHAT'S A CHICKEN?
PASTE
END

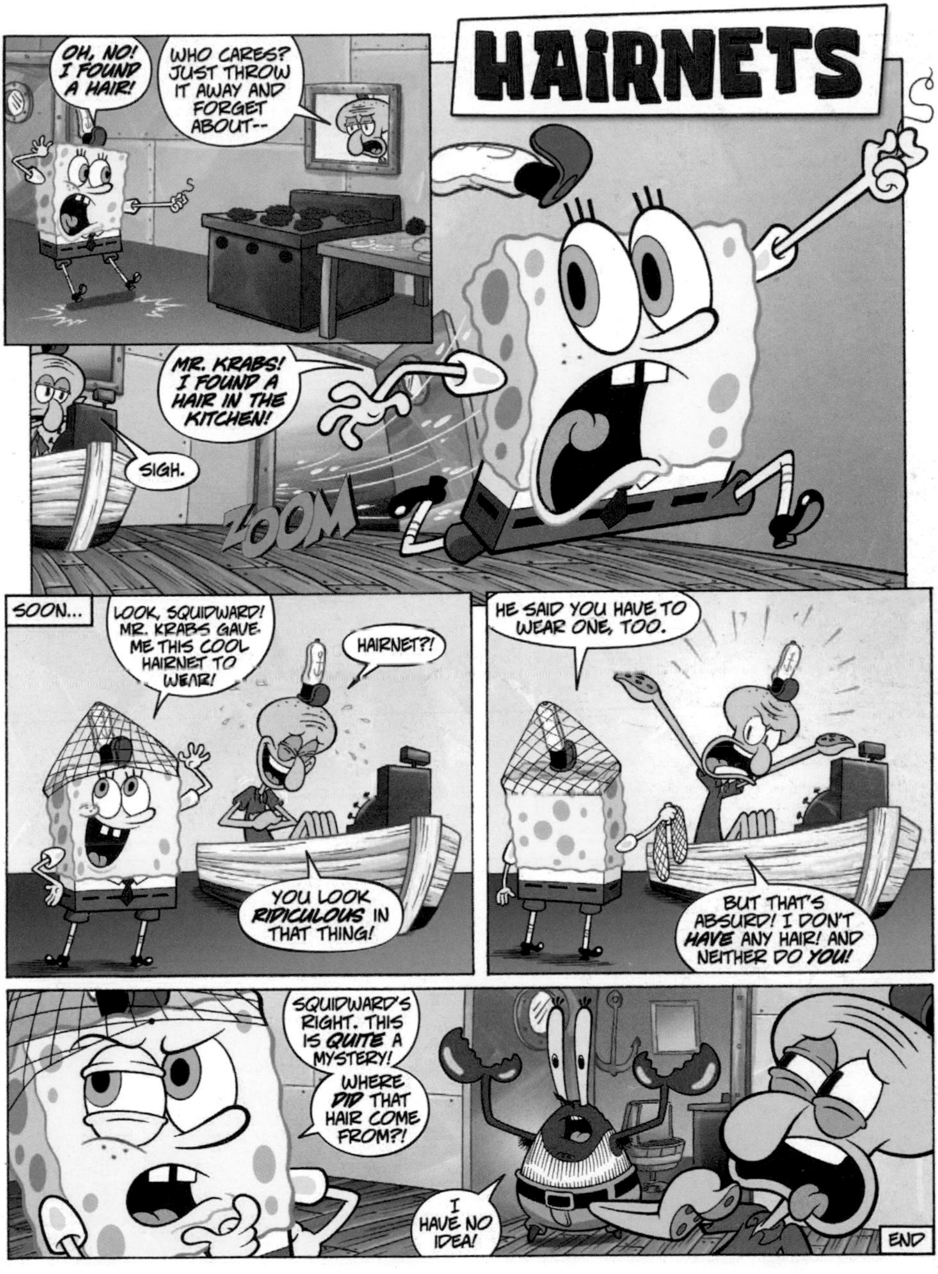

HAIRNETS

OH, NO! I FOUND A HAIR!

WHO CARES? JUST THROW IT AWAY AND FORGET ABOUT--

MR. KRABS! I FOUND A HAIR IN THE KITCHEN!

SIGH.

ZOOM

SOON...

LOOK, SQUIDWARD! MR. KRABS GAVE ME THIS COOL HAIRNET TO WEAR!

HAIRNET?!

YOU LOOK *RIDICULOUS* IN THAT THING!

HE SAID YOU HAVE TO WEAR ONE, TOO.

BUT THAT'S ABSURD! I DON'T *HAVE* ANY HAIR! AND NEITHER DO *YOU!*

PERMANENT BUBBLES

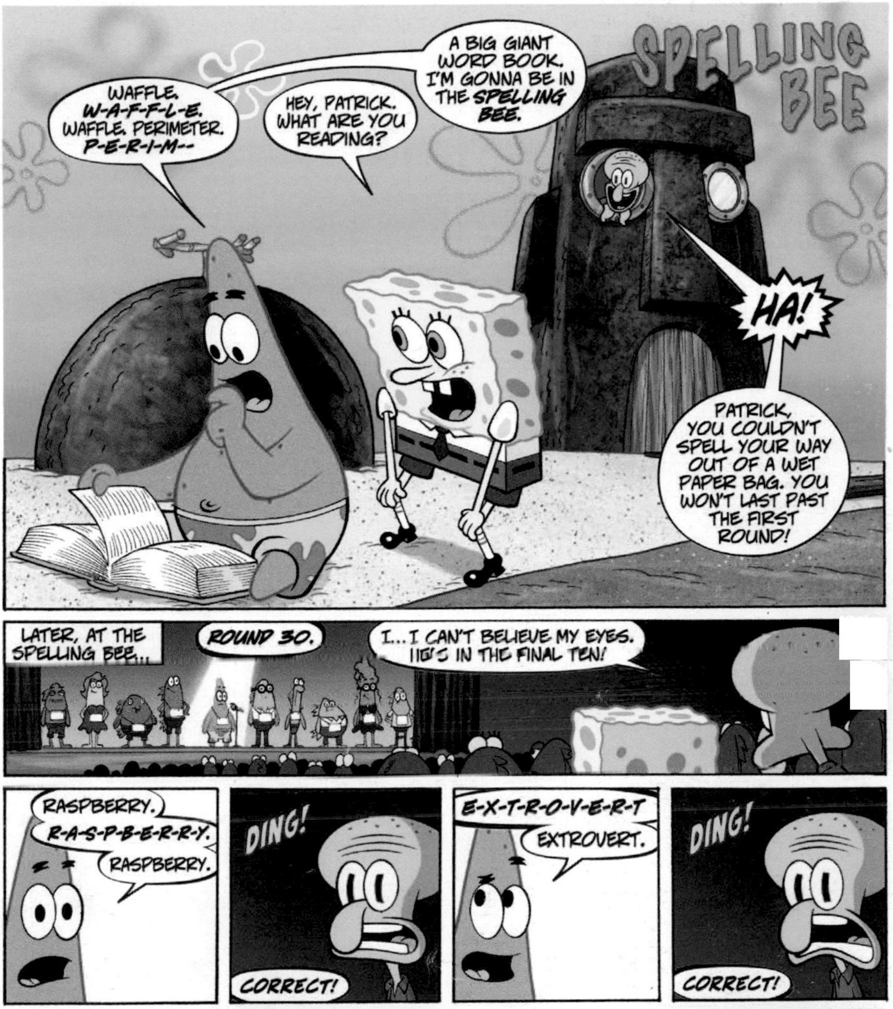

SPELLING BEE

WAFFLE. W-A-F-F-L-E. WAFFLE. PERIMETER. P-E-R-I-M--
HEY, PATRICK. WHAT ARE YOU READING?
A BIG GIANT WORD BOOK. I'M GONNA BE IN THE SPELLING BEE.
HA!
PATRICK, YOU COULDN'T SPELL YOUR WAY OUT OF A WET PAPER BAG. YOU WON'T LAST PAST THE FIRST ROUND!

ROCK.
UM... COULD YOU DEFINE THE WORD?

THE SOLID MINERAL MATERIAL THAT FORMS PART OF THE EARTH'S SURFACE.
COULD YOU USE IT IN A SENTENCE?

YOU, PATRICK STAR, LIVE UNDER A ROCK.
WORD ORIGIN, PLEASE?

CAN HE BE SERIOUS? THIS WORD STUMPS HIM?!
FINAL ROUND. LOTS OF PRESSURE.

OKAY...
ROCK.
R...
...A-O...
...U...
...3...
...P-L-K...
...C-H-36.
ROCK.
18
HA!!

DING!
CORRECT!

WAIT, WHAAAT?!?!
HE WON!
WHO'S THE MORON WHO'S JUDGING THIS THING?!

HI. I'M ROY.
E-N-D

Tape Shenanigans
By Graham Annable
Hey, SpongeBob! What are you doing with those seanut butter sandwiches?
They're a gift for Squidward! He's been so grumpy lately. I thought these might cheer him up!
Fold! Crease! Fold!
And now, just a smidgen of tape!
Zziiik!
Tik!
Pat! Smooth! Pat!
Look, Sponge Bob!
Tape has all kinds of uses!
Let me try!
Ziik!
Zik! Pat! Pat! Pull! Tik!

Ta da!

HA HA
HA HA
HA HA
HA

More!
More!
ZIK!

I've run out of kelp powder and the store's closed. I'll have to borrow some of SpongeBob's. How humiliating!

KNOCK!
KNOCK!

Hu-whoa Squithwerth! Huh nith of yoo to dropth by!

YAAAAAH!

Waith! I have a nith gifth forr yoth!

Ackthoo-lee, I don'th think Squithwerth even liketh theanut buther sandwithes!
Whath arr yoth sayinth Pah-thrick? I canth unnersthand yoth!

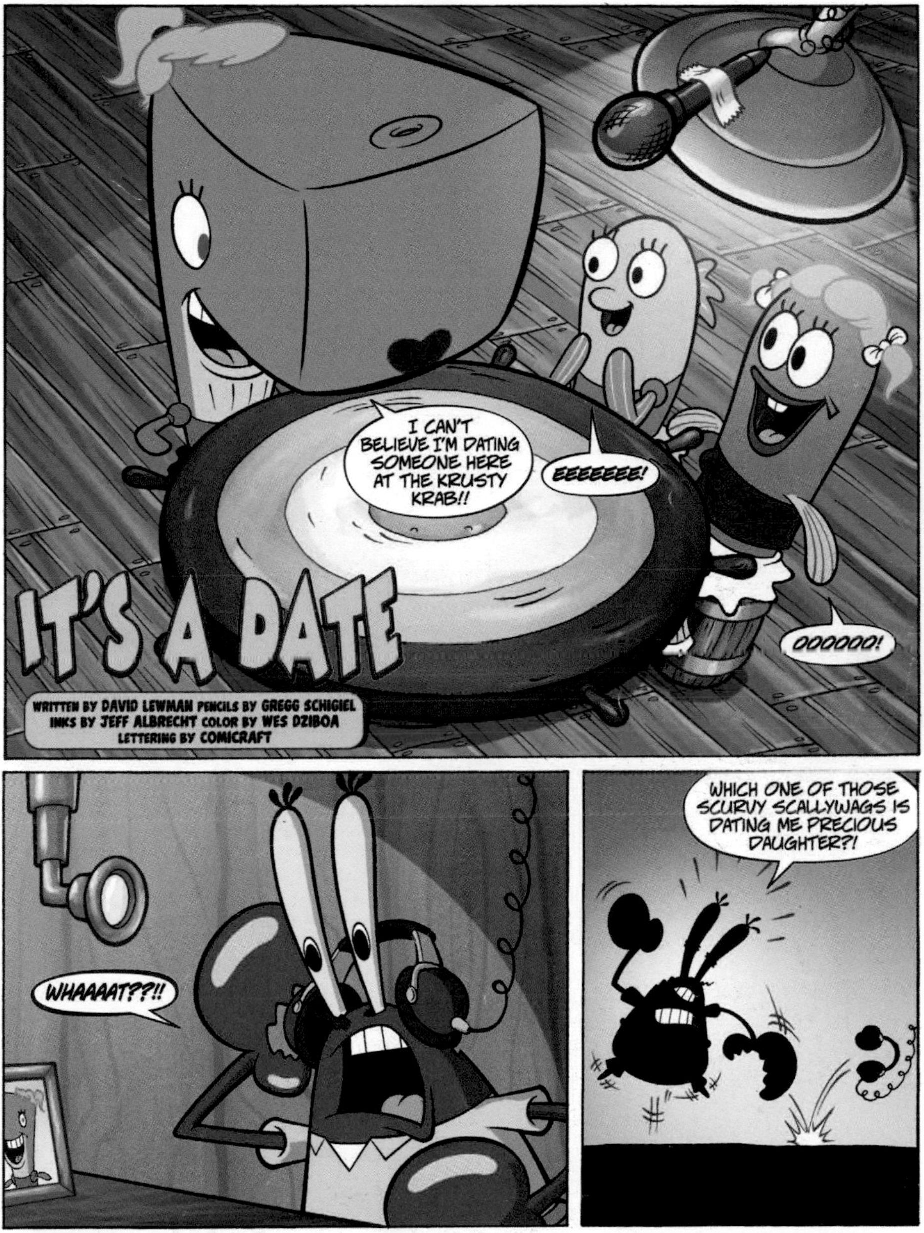

I CAN'T BELIEVE I'M DATING SOMEONE HERE AT THE KRUSTY KRAB!!
EEEEEEE!
OOOOOO!

IT'S A DATE

WRITTEN BY DAVID LEWMAN PENCILS BY GREGG SCHIGIEL
INKS BY JEFF ALBRECHT COLOR BY WES DZIBOA
LETTERING BY COMICRAFT

SQUIDWARD! WHERE'S PEARL?
SHE AND HER FRIENDS JUST LEFT. HOW I ENVY THEM.
SIGH...

OH, SO YEH NOTICED PEARL LEAVIN', DIDJA?
I ALWAYS NOTICE WHEN SOMEONE ESCAPES THIS DUMP.

SO, UH, WHAT DO YOU THINK O' ME DAUGHTER, PEARL?
NOTHING. EXCEPT THAT I WISH I WERE HER.

YOU MEAN YEH WISH YOU WERE A GIRL?
NO, I WISH I WASN'T HERE.

OH, SPONGEBOB...

YOU KNOW ME DAUGHTER, PEARL?
I SURE DO, MR. KRABS!
AND WHAT DO YOU THINK OF HER?
I THINK SHE'S THE MOST FANTASTIC DAUGHTER YOU EVER HAD!

SHE'S THE *ONLY* DAUGHTER I EVER HAD.
OH, YEAH.

SO YOU LIKE PEARL, EH?
UH, SURE, MR. KRABS. SHE'S THE *PEARLIEST!*

AH-HA!

THAT CLINCHES IT...
WHAT WAS *THAT* ALL ABOUT?

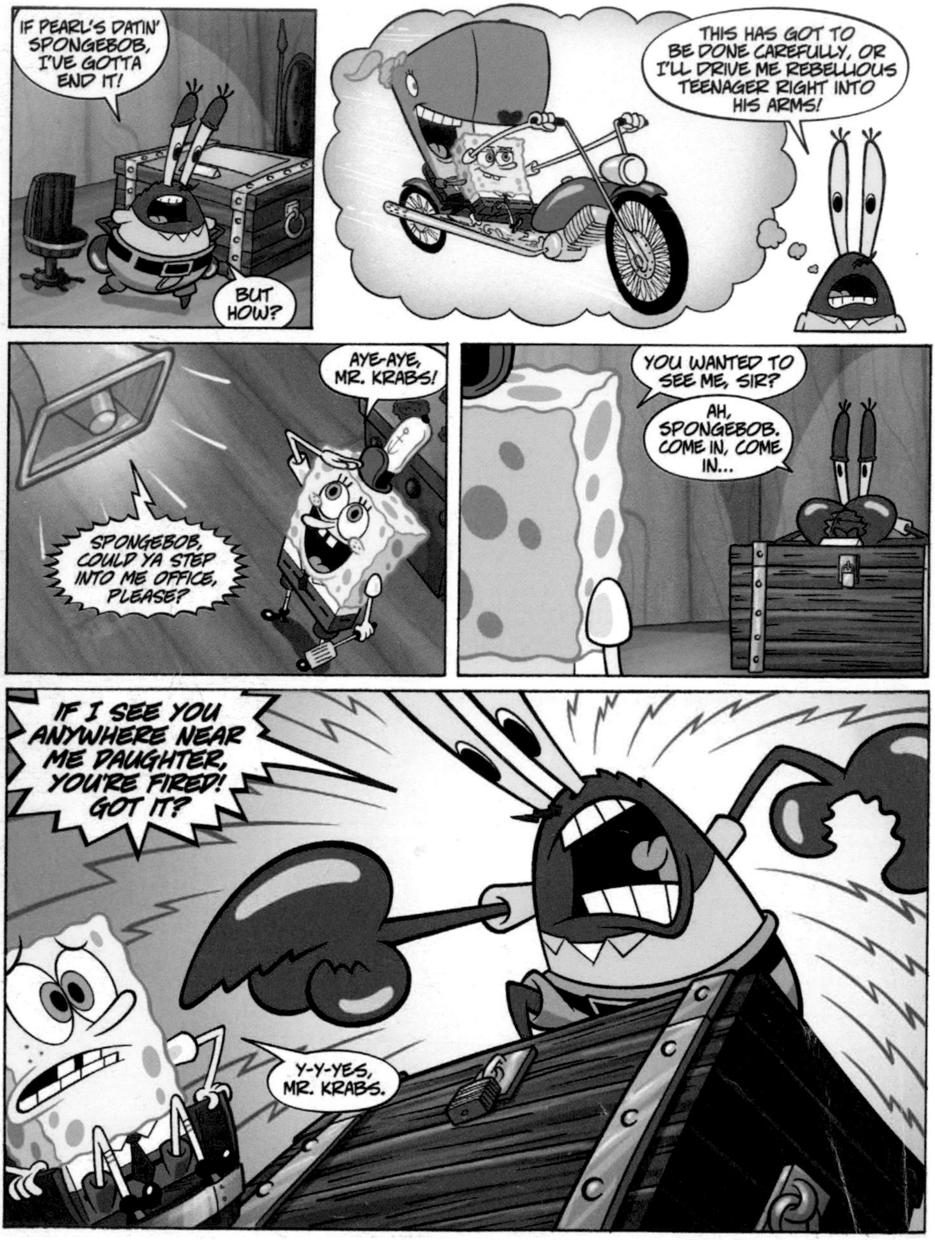

IF PEARL'S DATIN' SPONGEBOB, I'VE GOTTA END IT!
BUT HOW?

THIS HAS GOT TO BE DONE CAREFULLY, OR I'LL DRIVE ME REBELLIOUS TEENAGER RIGHT INTO HIS ARMS!

SPONGEBOB, COULD YA STEP INTO ME OFFICE, PLEASE?
AYE-AYE, MR. KRABS!

YOU WANTED TO SEE ME, SIR?
AH, SPONGEBOB. COME IN, COME IN...

IF I SEE YOU ANYWHERE NEAR ME DAUGHTER, YOU'RE FIRED! GOT IT?
Y-Y-YES, MR. KRABS.

PEARL!!!

HI, SPONGEBOB!

PEARL!!!
HI, SPONGEBOB!
PEARL!!!
HI, SPONGEBOB!
PEARL!!!
HI, SPONGEBOB!
PEARL!!!
HI, SPONGEBOB!
PEARL!!!
FLUSHHH
HI, SPONGEBOB!

HI, SPONGEBOB!
HI, PATRICK.

WHAT ARE YOU DOING HERE?
HIDING FROM PEARL! I NEVER KNOW WHERE SHE'LL SHOW UP!

WHY DON'T YOU FOLLOW HER? THEN YOU'LL KNOW RIGHT WHERE SHE IS!
PATRICK, YOU'RE A GENIUS!
NO, SPONGEBOB. I'M A STARFISH.

THERE'S PEARL!
HERE'S CORAL!

THERE'S NO WAY SHE CAN SURPRISE ME NOW, AND I WON'T HAVE TO HEAR THOSE AWFUL WORDS--

YOU'RE FIRED!!
YAAAAH!

PLEASE, MR. KRABS! DON'T FIRE ME! PLEASE!

I TOLD YOU NOT TO DATE ME DAUGHTER, SPONGEBOB!
EWWW.
I'M NOT DATING SPONGEBOB.

BUT YOU SAID YOU WERE DATING SOMEONE AT THE KRUSTY KRAB.
I AM...

...HIM!
ROBBIE FROM SCHOOL! WE HAVE A DATE HERE AT THE KRUSTY KRAB.
OHHHH!

WE ONLY CAME HERE BECAUSE ROBBIE LOVES SPONGEBOB'S KRABBY PATTIES.
YOU HEARD HER, BOY! START GRILLIN' THEM PATTIES!
YES, SIR!

SAY, DID THAT YOUNGSTER ALREADY PAY FER HIS PATTIES?
IN CASH.
GOOD.

BOOOT
NOBODY DATES ME DAUGHTER!
THE END

DON'T MISS

Nickelodeon
SpongeBob SquarePants
Mermaid to Measure

Nickelodeon
SpongeBob SquarePants
Jellyfish Fields
Gone Jellyfishing

OUT NOW!

WWW.TITANBOOKS.COM

© 2010 Viacom International Inc. All Rights Reserved. Nickleodeon, SpongeBob SquarePants and all related titles, logos and characters are trademarks of Viacom International Inc. Created by Stephen Hillenburg.

MORE MARINE MAYHEM!

AVAILABLE NOW!